The Garland Library
of Medieval Literature

General Editors
James J. Wilhelm, Rutgers Univesity
Lowry Nelson, Jr., Yale University

Literary Advisors
Ingeborg Glier, Yale University
Guy Mermier, University of Michigan
Fred C. Robinson, Yale University
Aldo Scaglione, University of North Carolina

Art Advisor
Elizabeth Parker McLachlan, Rutgers University

Music Advisor
Hendrik van der Werf, Eastman School of Music

On the right is the reverse of the Great Seal of King Henry II of England showing the king in full armor, including a helmet with nasal. On the left is the ship seal of Dunwich, 1199, showing the castles that have been added fore and aft.

(The seals were reproduced in wax by Alexander and Julie Wieber; the photography is by Philip Blakenship)

The Rise of Gawain, Nephew of Arthur (De ortu Waluuanii nepotis Arturi)

edited and translated by
M ILDRED L EAKE D AY

Volume 15
Series A
G ARLAND L IBRARY OF M EDIEVAL L ITERATURE

Garland Publishing, Inc.
New York and London
1984

Library of Congress Cataloging in Publication Data

De ortu Waluuanii nepotis Arturi. English & Latin.
The rise of Gawain, nephew of Arthur = De ortu
Waluuanii nepotis Arturi.

(The Garland library of medieval literature ; v. 15.
Series A)
Text and translation of De ortu Waluuanii nepotis
Arturi from the British Library codex Cotton Faustina
B vi.
Medieval romance in Latin prose attributed to Robert
de Torigni.
Bibliography: p.
Includes index.
1. Gawain—Romances. 2. Arthurian romances. I. Day,
Mildred Leake, 1929–   . II. Robert, de Torigni,
d. 1186. III. Title. IV Title: De ortu Waluuanii
nepotis Arturi. V. Series: Garland library of medieval
literature ; v. 15.
PA8810.D38E5 1984   821′.1   83-48237
ISBN 0-8240-9423-9 (alk. paper)

Printed on acid-free, 250-year-life paper
Manufactured in the United States of America

The Garland Library of Medieval Literature

Preface of the General Editors

The Garland Library of Medieval Literature was established to make available to the general reader modern translations of texts in editions that conform to the highest academic standards. All of the translations are original, and were created especially for this series. The translations attempt to render the foreign works in a natural idiom that remains faithful to the originals.

The Library is divided into two sections: Series A, texts and translations; and Series B, translations alone. Those volumes containing texts have been prepared after consultation of the major previous editions and manuscripts. The aim in the editing has been to offer a reliable text with a minimum of editorial intervention. Significant variants accompany the original, and important problems are discussed in the textual notes. Volumes without texts contain translations based on the most scholarly texts available, which have been updated in terms of recent scholarship.

Most volumes contain Introductions with the following features: (1) a biography of the author or a discussion of the problem of authorship, with any pertinent historical or legendary information; (2) an objective discussion of the literary style of the original, emphasizing any individual features; (3) a consideration of sources for the work and its influence; and (4) a statement of the editorial policy for each edition and translation. There is also a Select Bibliography, which emphasizes recent criticism on the works. Critical citations are often accompanied by brief descriptions of their importance. Selective glossaries, indices, and footnotes are included where appropriate.

The Library covers a broad range of linguistic areas, including all of the major European languages. All of the important literary forms and genres are considered, sometimes in anthologies or selections.

The General Editors hope that these volumes will bring the general reader a closer awareness of a richly diversified area that has for too long been closed to everyone except those with precise academic training, an area that is well worth study and reflection.

James J. Wilhelm
Rutgers University

Lowry Nelson, Jr.
Yale University

For all my team:
my parents, Howard and Marjory Leake;
my sons and daughters,
Marjory, Jim, Susan, Howard and Roger;
and my husband Jim

CONTENTS

xi

BM Cotton Faustina B vi, f. 22v to 23r. *De ortu Waluuanii* begins in the far right column, following the end of the romance *Historia Meriadoci*, probably by the same author. (Reproduced from microfilm by permission of the British Library)

Introduction

Authorship and Dating

De ortu Waluuanii nepotis Arturi is an exciting adventure story of the training, testing, and recognition of Gawain, the earliest paragon of knighthood in King Arthur's court. The setting is the historical world of the fifth century: Rome, Jerusalem, Britannia. At least one copy of the story circulated in England, apparently influencing *Sir Gawain and the Green Knight* and *The Faerie Queene*, Book I. Yet the story is not well known. J. Douglas Bruce edited it in 1898 and 1913, but no English translation has been published other than in dissertation form (see Wieber and Day in Select Bibliography for details). Nevertheless it is a significant part of the "Matter of Britain," both as a background for the character of Gawain and as an intermediary form between the chronicles and the romances.

The single extant copy of *De ortu Waluuanii*, British Museum Cotton Faustina B vi, 23r–38r, is written in a hand of the first quarter of the fourteenth century. The date of the original composition is debated, but internal evidence suggests the last quarter of the twelfth century. The manuscript gives no indication of its author other than the initial "R" on the preceding story, *Historia Meriadoci*, considered to be by the same writer. John Bale lists *De ortu Waluuanii* under the works of Robert of Mont St. Michel in his index of British writings published in 1559. Robert, also known as Robert of Torigni, was abbot of Mont St. Michel from 1154 to 1186 and a historian of the reign of Henry II.

For this information Bale cites the Norwich catalog in his autograph notebook (p. 384) and the catalog of Boston of Bury in his completed work (1559, 2.131). Bruce, unaware of Bale's citation when he edited *De ortu Waluuanii* (hereafter written *DOW*) in 1898, proposed as author an unknown English clerk of the thirteenth century living in the southwest of England. Even after Margaret Shove Morriss had drawn scholarly attention to Bale's citation, Bruce, in his works of 1913 and 1928, persisted in his original theory of authorship, and most scholars followed him, rejecting Robert's authorship either because of the early date required or because of the difference in style between his known historical writing and the romance. Yet details of costume and ship construction suggest a possible twelfth-century date of composition, and the way Gawain's boyhood is presented is unique in its historical approach. The authorship of Robert deserves reconsideration.

Robert's career was exemplary as an abbot and a scholar. His name first appears in 1128, when he enrolled in the Benedictine monastery and school at Bec. In 1139 he was monastery librarian. It was Robert who was responsible for showing the copy of Geoffrey of Monmouth's *Historia Regum Britanniae* to Henry of Huntingdon. Henry of Huntingdon relates the incident, the earliest recorded mention of Geoffrey's work, in his introductory remarks to "Letter to Warinus," his summary of the *Historia* (Delisle, 1.97–119). In 1154 Henry II concurred in Robert's election as abbot of Mont St. Michel, a religious position of considerable esteem. Robert's term of office was a strong one in the history of the abbey. The number of resident monks doubled; major rebuilding was accomplished; its reputation for learning in classics and sciences—medicine, astronomy, music—was pervasive. The abbey was host to Henry II on a number of occasions, and once in 1158 both Henry and Louis VII were guests. Abbey business also required Robert to travel to England (Gout, 1.141–55).

Though Robert's seventeenth-century biographer, Dom Jean Huynes, records an extravagant tradition that Robert wrote 140 books, the list of his extant known writings is still impressive (Howlett, xvi): 1. Additions to William of Jumièges, including the eighth book in its entirety; 2. *Roberti Accessiones ad Sigebertum* (his *Chronicle*); 3. *Chronicon Beccense*; 4. *Continuatio Beccensis*; 5. *Annals of Mont St. Michel*, 1135–1173; 6. *Rubrica Abbreviata*; 7. The prologue to an edition of Pliny's *Natural History*; 8. The prologue to a collection of extracts from St. Augustine, which he discovered to have been wrongly attributed to Bede; 9. The catalog of the library at Bec. Of these works the best known is the *Chroni-*

cle, which was organized as a continuation of the universal history of Sigebert of Gembloux, covering the events of the reigns of Stephen and Henry II and including, like Sigebert's, the events of other kingdoms, ranging as far as Jerusalem. Robert is considered a major historian of his period.

In general the style of Robert's *Chronicle* is plainer than the style of *DOW*. The sentences are shorter and the verb frequently falls in the position natural to French, while in *DOW* the sentences are more often complex or compound-complex with the principal verb in the final position. Pio Rajna (1930, pp. 236–37) emphasizes that a difference in style does not necessarily indicate a different author, merely a different genre; Robert could have written in a more elaborate style for a romance. Actually in two specific passages Robert's style in his chronicles is quite like the style in *DOW*. For example, the entry in the *Chronicle* on the Battle of Lincoln in 1141 is written in verse, as are the descriptions of the battles on the Barbarous Isle in *DOW*. Robert uses the metaphor of the fighting boar in these rhyming couplets much as the author of *DOW* does for the action of the first day of single combat. Another example is found in the *Continuatio Beccensis*, or chronicle continuation, for 1158, under Howlett's heading "Subjugation of Wales" (p. 318), where Robert writes, "Henricus, rex Anglorum, omni Wallia sibi subjugata et facta tributaria," the same pattern of naming the king who subdues the entire nation and exacts tribute that appears in the opening lines of the *DOW*: "Uterpendragon rex pater Arturi omnium Britannie confinium provinciarum sue dicioni reges subegerat tributariosque efficiens." The similarity of these two passages probably rests on a convention for describing successful conquests. The author of *DOW* seems to have deliberately opened his romance with the kind of introductory statement usually found in a chronicle. While these touches of stylistic similarity between Robert's known works and *DOW* do not of themselves indicate that the same hand wrote both, they do show that the difference in style between them is not as absolute as Bruce (1913, pp. xiii–xiv) intimated.

Bruce also rejected the possibility of Robert's authorship because the twelfth-century date for a Latin work did not fit his theory of the evolution of Arthurian romance from written French originals. In his 1898 edition (pp. 388–89) he proposed a French verse original for *DOW* composed in the later twelfth or early thirteenth century. He concluded that the Latin romance was then "worked up" in the second quarter of the thirteenth century.

After the challenge to his thirteenth-century theory that Bale's citation of Robert posed, Bruce reissued his editions of *DOW* and *Historia Meriadoci* with a revised introduction. Bruce suggested three possible stemmatic clues to support his earlier position (1913, p. xxiii). One is what he calls the "trick" of ascribing to the hero the first use of something. In *DOW* Gawain is the first knight to wear a surcoat over his armor, and he is known as "Miles cum tunica armature" (Knight of the Surcoat) until Arthur reveals his true name. Bruce proposes that this "trick" was borrowed from the prose *Lancelot*, dated 1215–30, in which Lancelot is noted as the first man to wear a pennon on his helmet. Yet in *DOW* the first use of the surcoat is integral to the story, while in *Lancelot* the first use of the pennon is only a briefly noted detail. Bruce's other stemmatic clues are the names "Nabaor" and "Buzafarnan." In *DOW* Nabaor is the servant and adviser to the queen of Milocrates, the pirate king. He is a valuable ally of Gawain. Bruce proposes that the name "Nabaor" was borrowed from the prose *Tristan*, dated 1215–35, in which the giant is named "Nabon." Bruce also notes possible variations of "Nabaor" in other romances, but in no romance does the character have a role equivalent to the Nabaor of *DOW*. The second name, "Buzafarnan," is the pirate sea-captain in *DOW*, brother of King Milocrates. This name Bruce considers a corruption of "Nabuzardan," the treacherous brother in the prose *Tristan*.

Ernst Brugger challenged Bruce on the value of either of these names as stemmatic evidence. Brugger points out that "Nabaor" as a variant of "Nabon" is derived from the pagan god Mabon and as such is part of the general mythological material available to medieval storytellers. Similarly Brugger traces "Buzafarnan/Nabuzardan" to variations of the Hebrew "Nebuchadnezzar," again denying to Bruce the validity of these names for dating *DOW*.

Even though Rajna and Brugger had indicated that Bruce's arguments against a twelfth-century date and Robert's authorship were not unassailable, R. S. Loomis in *Arthurian Literature in the Middle Ages* follows Bruce in assigning a thirteenth-century date to *DOW*, saying that the ascription of the romance to Robert of Torigni was "absurd" (p. 473). Loomis concedes that, "in spite of its late date and its idiosyncrasies, *De ortu Waluuanii* preserves a good deal of the old story of Gawain" (p. 476), but his final evaluation is that the Latin romance is largely a rhetorical exercise.

No compelling need exists to label a romance written in Latin in either the twelfth or thirteenth century as a "working up" of written French sources, as Bruce insists, or as a "rhetorical exercise," as Loomis terms it. Original Latin literature of all kinds, poetry and prose, was being composed during this period, particularly in the twelfth century. A broad and international audience for Latin literature existed in the monasteries, the universities, and the royal courts. Henry II is remembered for being "literatus," fluent in Latin.

DOW is in some details more primitive than would be expected of a translation of a late twelfth- or early thirteenth-century French romance. Rajna (1930, pp. 243–44) notes the primitive quality of Arthur's court, where horses can be brought into the royal sleeping chamber or an envoy from Rome be received by a king holding court outside under an ash tree. Rajna also points out that Kay lacks the rudeness of the developed French tradition, Arthur's queen is a sorceress named Guendoloena (a name and characterization not found elsewhere), and Arthur himself is a fighting king, proud of being without a peer among his own knights. In regard to the pride of Arthur *DOW* is similar to Robert Biket's *Lai du Cor*, the earliest extant lai, possibly from the third quarter of the twelfth century (Hoepffner, pp. 113–16). Arthur's pride becomes a problem in the last part of *DOW*, just as it does in the *Lai du Cor*, and the problem is resolved in a similar way. In both tales Arthur is humiliated: in the *Lai du Cor* because he is drenched while drinking from the magic horn that spills over a man whose wife is unfaithful and in *DOW* because, in challenging Gawain at the ford, Arthur is unhorsed and has to walk back to Caerleon, again thoroughly drenched. In both tales Arthur saves face because all of the court must finally share his embarrassment: in the *Lai du Cor* because the wine spills over each of the knights except Garadue, in *DOW* because Gawain proves that he can outfight not merely any of Arthur's knights but all of them together when he rescues the lady of the Castle of Maidens singlehandedly. Finally *DOW* is primitive with regard to thirteenth-century French romances in two other aspects. The character of Gawain is above reproach, and there is no courtly love at all.

Details from the text itself—costume, armor, naval technology, political concerns—suggest a twelfth-century origin. These include the surcoat for armor, helmets with nasals, ship designs, use of both rams and Greek fire in naval battle, a Jerusalem besieged but not yet captured, and the triumph by the British at the Castle of Maidens. Costume and armor form the first pair of details that provide a spread of years for a possible date. The surcoat that is Gawain's identifying garment in *DOW* was a costume adopted by the crusaders that came into use in the twelfth century and became very popular in the thirteenth, being worn by everyone—civilian and military, male and female. That the costume is considered unique in the story, unique enough to supply Gawain's soubriquet, suggests that the garment is familiar to the audience but is still distinctive. William B. Mullen (pp. 74–78), who studied the mention of the surcoat (*Waffenrock*) in early German literature, concludes that the garment first appeared in the latter half of the twelfth century and came into general use a little before 1200. He feels that a romance in which a hero could be identified by such a garment would have been written about 1200 rather than later.

Though the surcoat is a distinctive new garment in *DOW*, the armor described is of a style passing out of use in the thirteenth century. The armor of the forester on the Barbarous Isle includes a helmet with nasal. So does the helmet of the splendid gilded armor of Milocrates that the queen gives to Gawain. The nasal is not merely descriptive but functional. Gawain grasps the forester's helmet by the nasal in order to drag the body. In the battle with Milocrates the nasal on the helmet that Gawain is wearing protects him from a fatal slash across the face. While both incidents are verbal echoes of Geoffrey of Monmouth's *Historia* (8.4; 9.7), that the author of *DOW* chose to use the helmet with nasal in such concrete ways indicates that this style of helmet and its advantages were familiar.

The helmet with nasal was in general use in the twelfth century, as is evidenced by the Great Seal of Henry II (frontispiece) that shows Henry in full armor, including a profile view with nasal outlined. The open helmet with a nasal began to be replaced by the helmet with complete face protection toward the end of the twelfth century. As R. C. Smail explains in *Crusading Warfare* (*1097–1193*): "At the end of the century men who could afford to do so had replaced the conical helmet with nasal by the pot helm" (p. 107). Although helmets with nasals continued to be worn and persisted in romances as late as *Claris et Laris*, (lines 475–80), dated 1286, the helmet with nasal that Gawain wears is more than an ordinary piece of armor; it is the helmet included in the royal attire of gilded armor. Such an outfit must fit the concept of splendor for its time. For the thirteenth century splendid armor included a visored helmet; for most of the twelfth century a helmet with nasal was the finest available.

While the question of dating the surcoat and the helmet is developed by Morriss, Bruce (1913), and Mullen, the possibility of determining a date for *DOW* from the description of the ships has not been previously considered. The structures of various ships described in *DOW* suggest a twelfth-century origin. First, all the ships described, whether merchant or naval vessels, can be beached. The merchant ship carrying the infant Gawain is beached near Narbonne, and the entire fleet from Rome is beached on the shore of the Barbarous Isle. The ships are of shallow enough draft that they can be carried upstream and arranged as a makeshift defense with the prows pointing outward. In the twelfth century ships were built for easy beaching. Richard Unger, in *The Ship in Medieval Economy, 600–1600* (p. 77), describes cargo and naval vessels in use in northern Europe from the early Middle Ages through the twelfth century as being smaller than similar Roman vessels and generally adapted to either beaching or the use of tidal flats. In the thirteenth century, however, the cog—more seaworthy in design with the addition of a keel—became the merchant vessel of choice. The deeper draft and the keel made beaching less practical, and by 1250 most significant ports had quays. The older form of landing was still in some use; beaches at ports were kept open for Scandinavian warships and some cargo vessels. In *DOW*, where both merchant and naval vessels are beached without comment, a maritime technology is indicated that is more typical of the twelfth than the thirteenth century.

Gawain and the centurion modify their galley for greater fighting advantage before they leave the Barbarous Isle. They order a *turris* (castle) built on the poop of the galley. The structures known later as sterncastle and forecastle were first added to existing ships in the latter part of the twelfth century. Peter Kemp says that "forecastles and aftercastles . . . began to come in during the last years of the twelfth century as separate structures built on the deck inside the hull" (p. 59). Roger Anderson (1972, p. 401) comments, "There was little change in ship technology during the twelfth century apart from fitting of light 'castles' at either end of the larger vessels." The ship seal of Dunwich of 1199 (frontispiece) illustrates these structures added to an existing ship, while the ship seal of Dover of 1284 (Kemp, p. 59) shows them built into the hull as part of the original construction. The modification ordered by Gawain and the centurion would have been a significant addition in the twelfth century but redundant in the thirteenth.

Gawain's galleys are fitted with rams. The ram as a naval offensive weapon went out of use toward the end of the twelfth century. Anderson (1962, p. 59) observes that dated illustrations of Mediterranean galleys seem to show a modification of the classic ram into a bow with a beak toward the end of the twelfth century. He adds that the last recorded sinking of a vessel in combat using the ram was in 1191, when Richard the Lionhearted sank a very large Saracen dromon.

Gawain also confronts Greek fire as a naval weapon. Described in *DOW*, Greek fire is of the type that twelfth-century crusaders experienced: a terrifying fire weapon, possessed by the enemy alone, that flamed even on the water. By the thirteenth century the Franks also used the weapon and its shock value was lessened. Two details suggest a twelfth-century date for the weapon as described in *DOW*. In the first place the author of *DOW* introduces the fire weapon as "Greek fire," a term that he explains. The classic Latin term for a fire weapon was *incendiarium oleum*. The term "Greek fire" was a coinage of the twelfth century. For example, the author of *Itinerarium Regis Ricardi* (1.81) describes the use of fire by Moslems at the attack on Acre (4 October 1189) and explains the fire weapon as "oleum incendiarium quod vulgo ignem Graecum nominat" (incendiary oil that is commonly called "Greek fire") as if the term were perhaps unfamiliar to an audience of the twelfth century. A second detail that may suggest a possible date concerns the use of human blood in the formula. This ingredient is not common in fire formulas, but curiously it appears in the *Ancrene Riwle* (p. 149), whose author develops an analogy for the love of Christ from the intensity of Greek fire:

> Greek fire is made of a red-haired man's blood, and they say that nothing but urine, sand, or vinegar can quench it. This "Greek fire" is the love of Jesus Christ our Lord. And you shall

make it of a red man's blood, that is, of the blood of Jesus
Christ, reddened with His own blood on the cross. And some
say that He was red-haired, too.

The notion that Greek fire was made with the blood of a red-haired
man must have been in general circulation before the *Ancrene
Riwle* was composed. The *Ancrene Riwle* is usually dated in the
early thirteenth century.

The political concerns within the romance also seem to reflect
crises of the last quarter of the twelfth century. The essential art of
any historical romance is to dramatize the presentness of the past.
The author of *DOW*, shaping his romance to events of the fifth
century, would probably choose events similar to crises of his own
time. Specifically the Roman War with Persia is like the contemporary conflict with the Moslems, while the securing of the border of
Arthur's kingdom beyond the Castle of Maidens may reflect the
settlement of the ransom of William the Lion at the Treaty of
Falaise, which awarded Edinburgh Castle to Henry II. Gawain's
first quest is to settle the fate of Jerusalem in single combat. Prepa-
rations are under way to prepare the city for siege, so that if
Gawain should be defeated in the single combat the inhabitants
might hold out on their own. Morriss (p. 614) points out that the
situation is similar to that of Jerusalem under the crusaders before
1187, when Jerusalem fell to Saladin, never to be regained. That the
author of *DOW* portrays Gawain as relieving the threat to
Jerusalem rather than recapturing the city seems to indicate a plot
composed before 1187.

Gawain's second quest secures Arthur's northern border, re-
gaining for Arthur's kingdom the Castle of Maidens. Edinburgh
Castle, identified with the Castle of Maidens since 1140 (Loomis,
1955–56, pp. 141–43), came temporarily under the control of
Henry II as part of the settlement of the Rebellion, specifically as
the ransom of William the Lion, King of Scotland, at the Treaty of
Falaise in 1175. The Arthurian context is implied even in the text of
the treaty itself, which lists the castles that pass under the control of
Henry II: Roxburgh, Jedburgh, Berwick, Stirling—and "Castellum
Puellarum," the Castle of Maidens (Stones, pp. 6–7). Robert of
Torigni (Howlett, p. 268) also refers to the "Castle of Maidens"
rather than Edinburgh in recording his summary of the Treaty of
Falaise. Henry II did not hold Edinburgh long. In 1186 he returned

the castle to William as dowry for his bride. Later Richard the Lionhearted relinquished claims against the remaining castles in order to finance his crusade. Only for a brief period, from 1175 to 1186, did a Norman king, like Arthur, hold the Castle of Maidens.

If the threat to Jerusalem and the relief of the Castle of Maidens in *DOW* reflect political tensions of the court of Henry II, a date when the romance would be most relevant would be between 1175 and 1186. Details from costume and technology indicate a possible date of composition in the last quarter of the twelfth century. In the development of Arthurian romance the influences on *DOW* of Geoffrey of Monmouth's *Historia* or Biket's *Lai du Cor* are more apparent than Chrétien's work, also suggesting composition in the last quarter of the twelfth century. The time period falls within the last years of the career of Robert of Torigni. Did the renowned abbot of Mont St. Michel actually write *De ortu Waluuanii?* Without definitive evidence outside the text, the conclusion must be simply that we do not know. Bale's catalog sources indicate only that Robert was considered to be the author by the holders of the manuscripts. The author must have been a man much like Robert: fluent in Latin, knowledgeable in literature and history. Robert of Torigni remains the single most important name in considering the authorship of *De ortu Waluuanii.*

Artistic Achievement

By synthesizing the tales of Gawain with events of the fifth century, the author of *DOW* composed a romance of a texture different from other early romances, closer to the style of Geoffrey of Monmouth but still clearly fictional. His artistic intention is stated in the concluding sentence of the work: "Realizing that just as it is more decisive to take part in a battle than to record a battle, even so it is more difficult to compose a *historia* in a formal style than it is to present it in the words of common speech." He has not only given the tales the formality of Latin composition, he has presented them as a *historia*. To use Northrop Frye's terms from *Secular Scriptures* (p. 36), he has displaced the romantic tales in the direction of reality. He has done this by giving the tales a setting in the fifth-century world, linking them to events like the sack of Rome and the Roman war with Persia, and creating characters who must make decisions and await results. His artistic achievement must be assessed on how effective this narrative is. The author's formal Latin prose style is not easy to translate into English narrative. As Wieber (pp. 104–13) notes, the grammar is complex, the vocabulary is rich, and rhetorical figures are frequent. Each sentence in the Latin carries more of the action of the story than would an equivalent English sentence. Wieber (p. 111) suggests that the work was meant to be read by individuals rather than performed for a larger audience.

The settings of *DOW*, with the exceptions of Uther's court and the Barbarous Isle, can be plotted on a map. All of the narratives of Gawain's boyhood tell how he was trained in arms in Rome. *DOW* is specific about the route he took to get there as well as the places of his youthful adventures. The merchants with the infant Gawain make their first landing at Narbonne. When Gawain leaves the emperor's court in Rome, he and his escort take ship at a port on the Adriatic Sea in order to sail for Jerusalem. When Gawain leaves Rome the second time, bound for Arthur's court, he takes the land route over the Alps and across Gaul. He apparently crosses the Channel and takes the land route again through the south of Britain because he is faced with fording the River Usk at the little town of Usk in order to get to Caerleon. Finally, in the last adventure at the Castle of Maidens (which the author specifies as being at the north of Britain), Gawain holds off the avenging pagans at a narrow bridge across a great ditch that marks the boundary—the most dramatic boundary ditch in that region being the remains of the Antonine Wall.

The plot involves actual events of the fifth century. The sack of Rome provides the opportunity for Viamundus to go to Rome with his stolen wealth and begin a new life without too many questions being asked. The Roman war with Persia provides a historical precedent for Gawain's single combat to settle a Persian conflict: Areobindus, a ranking military leader of the Eastern Roman forces, actually fought a Persian champion in single combat to decide the Persian war of 421–422 (Socrates, cols. 777–78). Gawain's military mission to aid Arthur was—in the mind of the emperor, at least—the final Roman aid to Britannia, date unknown.

The characters have been developed more realistically than the stock figures of romance. It is almost as if the author is reminding us not to judge a character until we know more about him. Viamundus, kidnapper and thief, receives the emperor's pardon for the responsible way he has managed Gawain's upbringing. Nabaor, spy for Milocrates, has his own reasons for betraying the pirate king. Princess Anna is in the end not disgraced for the illegitimate child she bore, but honored. The great Arthur is vulnerable in the area of his personal pride. Gawain must learn to balance his strength with sound planning, pain with renewed effort, and pride with patience.

The narrative tension that keeps the story moving is the result of the characters making decisions, having to choose between what is real and what is merely appearance. The most dramatic illustration of this is the scene on board the ship when the centurion and Gawain are watching the horizon. The centurion perceives a disturbance in the distance and decides that it is the wheeling of birds, an omen of a storm. Gawain, however, perceives the same disturbance as the banners on the mastheads of an approaching fleet, and he immediately warns his comrades of the approaching pirates. The real leadership of the group passes to Gawain at this point. Aubrey Galyon (pp. 336–39) comments, "In almost every part of the narrative both the action and the reader's interest depend upon one's judging that the appearance shows the reality. These actions that are based upon the conflict between appearance and reality are not auxiliary episodes in the romance. Rather they are the very stuff out of which the narrative fabric is woven." Galyon concludes that the author's concern with reality may even place the work much later, as part of the disputation over the theory of divine illumination that began with Richard of Middleton's *Quaestiones disputatae* of 1284.

Gawain's slaying of the great boar in the pirate king's forest serves as one of the controlling metaphors of appearance and reality. The boar, impaled on Gawain's hunting spear, can still attack. So also can King Milocrates, even though Gawain had left him unconscious on the ground after their first encounter. The attack by the pirates at sea follows the metaphor; although the land-based pirates are defeated, the pirates at sea can still attack in force. The author of *DOW* insists that the characters—and his readers—remember that appearance is not necessarily reality; down is not necessarily out; one's guard must be kept up.

The author's presentation of the bizarre formula for Greek fire is shaped by the same narrative technique as the romance itself: the decisions between appearance and reality are now expressed as decisions between hearsay and technology that the reader must make. In the episodes that precede the digression, the plot has followed the pattern of a hero tale. Gawain is born, grows up, and displays his extraordinary prowess as a knight. He is called upon for increasing courage and wisdom in each new crisis. But between his defeat of Milocrates on the Barbarous Isle and the slaying of Gormundus in single combat at Jerusalem the author presents Gawain with a challenge of a different order—the deadly weaponry of Greek fire projected by a ship at sea. To emphasize the difference and deadliness of the new weapon the author stops the action and describes its formula, processing, and projection in a digression that occupies more than a folio in the manuscript, some 110 lines in the present edition. The digression begins close to the center of the work. In the extant manuscript, where the story runs from folio 23r to folio 38v, the digression begins on folio 31v. It is clear that the author intends the digression on Greek fire to affect the reader's reaction to his romance. It does. The outlandish ingredients, the grisly description of the bloodletting, the primitive apparatus that suggests processing petroleum into gasoline, and the horror of the effectiveness of the new weapon cause a reaction from the reader of a different order from that of the adventures of Gawain. Bruce's reaction to the digression in his edition of 1898 is harsh: "It is inconceivable that a person who was capable of inserting into the romance the outrageously burlesque receipt for the preparation of Greek fire could have himself composed this interesting episode [the Barbarous Isle]" (p. 384). Bruce does not include the digression in his English paraphrases of the story for either of the editions.

But the author in episode after episode has reminded his characters and his readers to reserve judgment until all the facts are known. The first paragraph in the digression that contains the description of most of the bizarre ingredients is a parody in the style of the formula for Spanish gold in Theophilus' *De Diversis Artibus* (pp. 96–98), c. 1126, which begins with directions for breeding basilisks and ends with adding the blood of a red-haired man. Most of the bizarre ingredients in *DOW* can be found in Medea's cauldron in Ovid's *Metamorphoses* or among the stranger beasts in Pliny's *Natural History*. As Wieber (p. 60) notes, these ingredients are appropriately fiery. The phrase "oil of Medea," which according to J. R. Partington (p. 3) had been a term for petroleum since antiquity, may have suggested this fanciful introduction. Finally, before the reader becomes too smug with all this literary magic, the author concludes the paragraph with an authentic fire formula: "Sulphur . . . pix et resina, oleum, tartarum et bitumen" (sulphur, pitch and resin, oil, tartar, and petroleum).

These ingredients in various combination have been formulas for military fire since antiquity. Vegetius, in *Epitoma Rei Militari* 4.8, c. A.D. 380—90, mentions "bitumen, sulphur, picem liquidam, oleum." The *Mappae Clavicula*, items 266—79, has various fire formulas that the editors describe as "sticky, napalm-like" (note 185), containing naphtha or other kinds of oils. The manuscripts of the *Mappae* are from various periods, the oldest extant being tenth-century, with a tradition extending even earlier (3—5). The *Liber Ignium*, attributed to Marcus Graecus, has similar formulas. Formula 10 contains sulphur, resin, asphalt, sandarach (?), tartar, pitch, and dung, dissolved in petroleum. The oldest manuscript of the *Liber Ignium* is from the late thirteenth century (Partington, pp. 42—48).

The first paragraph in the digression in *DOW*, then, ends with a genuine formula for military fire. The next paragraph contains a grim description of the most effective way to take the blood from the red-haired man. Yet the author does not leave the reader altogether sure about the reality of this ingredient. He concludes by suggesting that the human blood must then be mixed with the blood of a dragon, showing again that appearance must be distinguished from reality. The paragraph that follows gives the classical Ovidian instructions for catching a dragon. Yet this bit of fantasy is immediately followed by descriptions of the apparatus for processing and projecting the fire. These are difficult to translate, perhaps confused in transmission, but whether the products of the author's imagination or garbled accounts of real technology, they represent a rare contemporary account of the processing and projecting of Greek fire. A vessel under pressure as described, fired with the intense heat of naphtha, could crack petroleum—if it did not explode first. Gasoline mixed with thickeners produces napalm. Partington has theorized that the difference between the traditional fire formulas and true Greek fire is not in some secret ingredient but in the distilling of the petroleum in the mix (pp. 31–32). The method of processing Greek fire in *DOW* seems to confirm his theory. The double-bellows pump in *DOW* for spraying the fire mixture is also significant. Byzantine sources name the device for projecting the fire as a *siphon*, but there is no single clear description of how the *siphon* operated. The pump described in *DOW* fits many of the details garnered by Partington from these sources (pp. 12–22). Again there is apparently no other contemporary description of the bellows method of spraying Greek fire.

The digression ends with a sober statement on the effectiveness of the weapon: "If you ask what power it has, no military machine is so strong, no ship so great but that if the fire is thrown it penetrates defenses and consumes everything on every side." All classical allusions, all technology, aside, this is the "infaustus ignis," the doomsday machine of its time (Evenhuis).

How does all this affect the actions of the hero? The pirates attack his ship with fire, the ship bursts into flame, Gawain leaps alone to the attacking ship, and he fights for the control of it. Some of the men he cuts to pieces; others he throws overboard. It is an extraordinary act of daring—but drowning the man operating a pump is not on the same order as meeting Gormundus in single combat. The opponent armed with the new technology is both greater and less than the heroic ideal. With the new technology of warfare represented by Greek fire the world of the story is no longer quite the world of Arthur and his knights. It is already, even in the twelfth century, the modern world, where warfare is impersonal and death holds no glory. Yet, once more a decision between appearance and reality must be made. With his ship on fire Gawain is, like the wounded boar, apparently down, but he is not out. He does what he must.

The artistic achievement of the author of *DOW* lies in the history that he created from the Gawain tales. Taking the tradition that Gawain was trained in arms at Rome, he retells Gawain's adventures as if he were a Roman cavalry officer rather than a knight errant. Gawain must learn courage and prowess at arms, but he must also learn the importance of military intelligence. Gawain's adventures are not random encounters but missions for the emperor of Rome. He has proper escort under the leadership of a centurion. His routes are the main travel routes of the time: by sea to Jerusalem, by land to Britain. Fifth-century Roman history underlies the main episodes of the story—the sack of Rome, the war with Persia, the final Roman aid to Britannia. The episode of Greek fire in the center of the work allows the reader to see how Gawain, functioning both as the Gawain of tradition and as the champion of Rome itself, can handle the threat of the awesome new weapon. The author has expanded the Arthurian world of the tales of Gawain to include more action, more tension, more humor, and more human understanding. An author who can compose an adventure story that holds readers in its created world for a space of time, and then returns them to the real world with a deepened sense of their own times, has written a story worth retelling, even centuries later.

Sources and Influences

No written source for the Arthurian material in *DOW* has been identified other than Geoffrey of Monmouth, *Historia Regum Britanniae*, but analogues can be traced in a number of romances. Like most of the extant Gawain romances, the story material in *DOW* is related to the adventures of Cuchulainn, particularly *Bricriu's Feast, The Violent Death of Curoi*, and *The Sickbed of Cuchulainn*. Basic research on analogues to *DOW* has been done by J. D. Bruce (1913, pp. xxv–lxiv), R. S. Loomis (1927, pp. 331–34; 1943, pp. 157–92), Helaine Newstead (pp. 811–15), V. J. Harward, Jr. (ch. 13), and J. L. Wieber (pp. 23–86). The influence of *DOW* on subsequent Arthurian romance has not previously been noted, but it may have suggested the gilded armor and royal red surcoat for Gawain's costume in *Sir Gawain and the Green Knight* as well as some features of the Red Cross Knight's three-day combat in *The Faerie Queene*, Book I.

There are four versions of Gawain's infancy: *Historia Regum Britanniae, Les Enfances Gauvain, Perlesvaus*, and *De ortu Waluuanii*. The *Historia* (8.21) tells of King Uther arranging the marriage of his daughter Anna to his ally Loth of Lodonesia. Their two sons are Gawain and Mordred (9.9). In the other three versions, however, Gawain is illegitimate. He is the child of Arthur's sister

(Morcades in *Les Enfances Gauvain*, Anna in *DOW*, unnamed in *Perlesvaus*) and Loth or Lot, variously identified as a king in *Perlesvaus*, a squire in *Les Enfances Gauvain*, and a hostage prince in *DOW*. The complex problem of identifying Gawain and his mother is handled by Rachel Bromwich (pp. 369–73).

In the three versions in which Gawain is illegitimate his birth must be kept secret. The infant is disposed of in *Les Enfances Gauvain* in a cask upon the sea, which is found by a fisherman. In *Perlesvaus* the infant is not exposed at sea but given to humble people to raise. In *DOW* he is given to foreign merchants to be raised in their native land. Bruce (1913, p. xli) suggests that these versions are related to the legend of Pope Gregory. Alan Markman (pp. 70–79) and Wieber (pp. 23–53) relate them to various Celtic *enfances*, or accounts of childhood.

All four versions of Gawain's infancy bring him to Rome. The *Historia* tells how he was sent by his father to serve in the household of Pope Sulpicius, who dubbed him a knight (9.11). In *Les Enfances Gauvain* the fisherman gives the boy to the pope to be educated and trained as a knight. In *Perlesvaus* his foster parents take him to the pope, who, on learning that he is the son of a king, receives him into his household. In *DOW* Viamundus, who stole the infant from the merchants, takes the boy with him when he begins a new life in Rome. On his deathbed he persuades the emperor to act as guardian.

The adventures that follow in *DOW* are not paralleled in any of the other accounts of Gawain's boyhood. *Les Enfances Gauvain* breaks off at this point; *Perlesvaus* has only a summary of the story of Gawain's infancy. Both romances suggest that Gawain may have become the emperor's heir, but *DOW* does not pursue the story in this direction. Instead *DOW* continues with a plot that follows the tradition of the "Fair Unknown," according to which the ruler makes a rash promise and an unknown, untried knight is given a significant quest. Bruce (1913, p. lv) suggests that the closest parallel to Gawain in *DOW* is a figure, Guinglain, in *Lybeaus Desconus*, a Middle English romance.

In *DOW* the delegation from Jerusalem arrives to plead for a champion so that the fate of the city may be decided by single combat rather than battle. Gawain immediately requests the venture, reminding the emperor of his promise. With both the rash

promise and the brash request Gawain's first quest of the romance
is initiated. As in *Hunbaut* and *The Turk and Gawain* (Thompson,
1979) Gawain has a companion and guide. In this case it is the
centurion. A date is assigned for completion of the quest, but it is
not the traditional "one year later" found in *Sir Gawain and the
Green Knight* or *The Wedding of Sir Gawain*. After Gawain and
the centurion take ship for the Holy Land, a storm arises—a conventional beginning of adventure in romances of all periods. The
island on which they find harbor is described as if it were the abode
of the Little People (Harward, ch. 13), but the author explains that,
although short, they are dangerous pirates. On the island Gawain
encounters a queen who has been influenced to fall in love with
him. Even though Gawain ignores her emotions, she betrays her
husband the king to him. The author explains that she had been
abducted by the pirate king and kept an unwilling prisoner. She
gives Gawain the magic armor that will be worn by the man who
slays the king and the sword that he must use. Analogies here are to
the cluster of stories dealing with the Green Lace/Magic Girdle as
well as to the fateful sword in *The Violent Death of Curoi* (Kittredge; Loomis, 1943; Day, 1984). Gawain wears the gilded armor
into battle against the king and beheads him with the sword.

After the island is brought under Roman control and the pirates
are defeated at sea, Gawain arrives at Jerusalem for the day appointed for single combat. The Persian champion is too big for a
horse to carry, and so the combat must be fought on foot. The duel
continues for three days. The episode does not seem to be a version
of the traditional three-day tournament, in which the hero wears a
different color each day; instead the duel seems more like a version
of the recurring three-day motif in the testing of the hero, as in tales
like *Bricriu's Feast*. Gawain slays the Persian champion and
Jerusalem is freed from the terror of the Persian army. Gawain
returns in triumph to the court of the emperor. With his return to
Rome the first quest is completed.

The second quest has a multiple motivation. The quest is initiated by Gawain's desire to fight for the famed King Arthur in
defense of Britannia, while the emperor—who alone knows
Gawain's lineage—plans to restore Britannia to the Roman Empire
through Gawain. Although the political motivation was probably
the author's addition, Gawain's high position in the empire is sug-

gested by both *Perlesvaus* and *Les Enfances Gauvain*. In the structure of the romance as a whole the purpose of the second quest is to restore the hero to his rightful identity and place.

Gawain journeys to Britannia, but before he can become one of Arthur's knights he must first gain Arthur's acceptance. The next episode begins with a bedroom conversation between Arthur and his queen, Guendoloena, like the one that initiates the action in *The Cattle Raid of Cooley*. The analogue in this case does not necessarily point to a Celtic origin because the literary tradition for this scene is widespread. For example, Darius and Atossa talk in bed in Herodotus (III, ch. 134). The motif appears in other Arthurian works: the third stanza of *Le Morte Arthur* and lines 7828 forward in *Lanzelet* (Bruce, 1913, p. lx). Like *DOW* each of these examples provides a "queen's taunt" that initiates subsequent events. In the course of the conversation in bed Guendoloena taunts Arthur with her foreknowledge of the young knight who will excel him in prowess. When she falls asleep, Arthur slips out and challenges the knight at the ford. An episode close to this is found in Heinrich von dem Türlin, *Diu Crône*, beginning with line 3424, in which the new knight is Gasozein (Bruce, 1913, p. lvii; Loomis, 1943, pp. 157–75; Kratz, pp. 351–56). In both encounters Arthur is unhorsed into the stream. A detail of the analogues that has not been noted is that, just as Gasozein in this episode is wearing the Magic Girdle, Gawain in *DOW* is wearing the gilded armor. Arthur catches sight of him by the gleam of his armor. The parallel suggests, as does the pirate queen's gift, that the gilded armor in *DOW* is a counterpart of the Magic Girdle/Green Lace motif.

By defeating King Arthur at the ford Gawain has embarrassed him, incurring the wrath of the man he had come so far to serve. Arthur refuses to allow Gawain to become one of his knights. Gawain then proposes for himself an "impossible task." He suggests that, if he can perform some exploit of arms that Arthur's entire band of knights cannot accomplish, then Arthur must accept him. Arthur agrees. The "impossible task" motif is like the "rash promise," a universal device of folklore for beginning an action. When the plea for help comes from the Castle of Maidens, events are set in motion for Gawain's final adventure.

Many romances link Gawain to the mysterious Castle of Maidens. Newstead proposes that the ultimate source for this part of the

Gawain tradition and the analogous adventures of other Arthurian knights is Celtic, related to *The Sickbed of Cuchulainn*. Newstead discusses *DOW* in connection with this tradition (pp. 812–13), saying that, although the plot of *DOW* shows some points of similarity with *Fergus* and the *Book of Gareth*, she agrees with Bruce that the closest analogues are *Yder*, lines 70–136, and the episode of Lufamour in *Sir Perceval of Galles*, beginning with line 955. In *DOW* Gawain rescues the Lady of the Castle of Maidens, and the story ends with King Arthur revealing to the young knight (known all this time only as "Knight of the Surcoat") that he is actually Gawain, son of his sister Anna and Loth, who are now king and queen of Norway.

While most scholarship on sources for *DOW* has been concerned with analogues of individual episodes, Raymond Thompson (1974) points out that the romance as a whole follows the mythological pattern of a hero tale. All the essential parts as specified by Otto Rank (p. 65) are present: distinguished parents, prohibited love, endangered infancy that often involves risk on water, nurture by humble people, and a return home, where the hero is acknowledged by a father-figure and achieves rank and honor. Thompson concludes that the antagonism between Arthur and Gawain in *DOW*, unusual in an Arthurian romance, stems from the roles of father-figure and hero inherent in the myth of the hero. Thompson also looks for the Oedipus feature of incest in the structure of *DOW*, suggesting that the episode with the queen of the Barbarous Isle may have been displaced or that Guendoloena's relationship to Gawain may have prefigured Guenivere and Lancelot. The threat of incest exists, however, without changing or expanding any elements of the plot. Making Gawain a rescuer of the lady of the Castle of Maidens immediately opens the threat of incest within the context of the Arthurian tradition. The lady of the Castle of Maidens is frequently Arthur's sister. Although usually the lady is Morgan the Fay, because of the identification of the Castle of Maidens with Edinburgh in Lothian, she is sometimes identified as Arthur's other sister, the wife of Loth and mother of Gawain. Sometimes Arthur's mother as well as his sister are in residence. In *Le Conte du Graal*, lines 7520–9168, Chrétien develops the tension of potential incest when Gawain, separated from his family since infancy, comes upon the castle where these women live (Busby, pp. 119–44).

The traditional structure of the plot of *DOW* can also be demonstrated with the code originated by Vladimir Propp to analyze folktales. *DOW* follows a familiar pattern that Propp called a "tale in two moves": it contains both the struggle-victory cluster of episodes and the difficult-task cluster, separated by a return home. Propp suggests that a "tale of two moves" may be considered a single tale when one move follows the conclusion of the other as a new shortage provokes a new quest (p. 104). The completion of the difficult task in *DOW* results in establishing Gawain's identity as Arthur's sister's son, providing closure to the problem of namelessness that Gawain has endured since childhood. *DOW*, ending with the recognition scene, lacks only the wedding and crowning common to most tales that Propp considered.

While the structure of the romance as a whole reveals a traditional unity, whether considered as a hero tale by Rank's definition or a classic folktale by Propp's, the analogues identified point to no single source. The author used the traditional material only as a base; apparently what was significant for him was how the adventures came about, given the context of the fifth century and the human motivation required.

The romance that resulted was different from other Arthurian romances in several respects. Because of its unusual approach tracing its influence ought to be easy, but apparently this version of Gawain's adventures was not widely imitated. However, the *Gawain*-poet and Edmund Spenser may have used a few details from *DOW* for their own highly individualized treatments of Arthurian legend. Like the hero of *Sir Gawain and the Green Knight* Gawain in *DOW* wears gilded armor and a red surcoat. The gilded armor appears first in lines 568–69, when the cloth covering is opened and spread out on the floor. Over this "gilded gear" Gawain wears a royal red surcoat, but the poet does not present the detail of costume specifically until he describes Gawain armed for the final encounter with the Green Knight, lines 2035–36, where Gawain has just wrapped the green girdle about his waist, "The girdel of grene silk, that gay wel besemed/upon that royal red clothe that rich was to shewe" (Jones, p. 109). The "royal red clothe" is the red surcoat.

One reason why the relationship between Gawain's costume in *DOW* and in *Sir Gawain and the Green Knight* has apparently not

been noted is that the Latin text states that the surcoat was "pur-pureus," which Bruce and others paraphrased as "purple." The *Oxford English Dictionary*, however, says that "purpureus" in the Middle Ages meant "crimson," or, as the *Gawain*-poet says, "royal red." Only in modern times did the term "purple" shift in meaning to reddish blue. Although the tradition of dressing Gawain like the earthly manifestation of the sun god may be part of the symbolic texture of *Sir Gawain and the Green Knight*, and Cuchulainn certainly dressed in a scarlet battle-apron in *The Cattle Raid of Cooley*, lines 2344–76, a Latin source for Gawain's costume was also available in *DOW*.

Establishing Spenser's possible use of *DOW* is more complex. To begin with, the plot of *The Faerie Queen*, Book I, is similar to that of *DOW*, but the similarity may rest simply on shared use of the conventions of Arthurian romance. The ten points of correspondence read like plot summaries. Both heroes are of noble lineage: Gawain is the nephew of Arthur; George is descended from a line of Saxon kings. Both are kidnaped as infants. Both are raised by poor men. As they attain manhood, both, though ignorant of their true lineages, are motivated to achieve prowess and fame. Each young man demands a boon of his sovereign, with the result that the sovereign is obligated to send an untried knight upon a serious quest. Gawain is sent to Jerusalem; George is sent to the Kingdom of Eden, which includes two traditional features of Jerusalem, the Well of Life and the Tree of Life. Both young knights are known only by the decoration of their armor: Gawain as Knight of the Surcoat, George as the Red Cross Knight. All the forces of evil are allied to prevent the heroes from achieving their quests. Because of wise companions the young men survive. Finally each young hero arrives at his destination to meet the final challenge alone, an individual combat that lasts for three days: Gawain with the giant Persian champion, George with the dragon.

Most of the common elements of plot belong to the general store of Arthurian material as identified on the previous pages, particularly the cluster of tales known as the "Fair Unknown." To establish an influence one must decide whether elements unique to *DOW* (that is, elements not part of conventional Arthurian material) are also found in Book I. Only one episode bears further investigation, the destination of the quest as Jerusalem or its equivalent and the three-day combat for its relief. The three-day combat

to relieve the siege of Jerusalem that the author of *DOW* created as the climax to Gawain's first adventure is not conventional in Arthurian tradition, as both Bruce (1913), pp. lx–lxi) and Wieber (p. 70) note. Bruce continues, however, to insist on a hypothetical French source, granting the author of *DOW* originality only in the battle rhetoric of the three-day combat. Spenser's destination for the Red Cross Knight is not specifically Jerusalem, either, but the Kingdom of Eden. Yet small details suggest a relationship between the two texts. Both authors begin each day of the three days of combat with a Virgilian sunrise. The second day in *DOW* begins "at Aurora's rising," the third when "the radiance of the sun had put to flight the darkness of the night." Spenser announces the second day with "The morrow gan early to appear/that Titan rose to run his daily race," and the third "The joyous day gan early to appear/And fair Aurora from the dewy bed of aged Tithon gan herself to rear/With rosy cheeks, for shame as blushing red."

The combatants of *DOW* receive little special treatment between the days of fighting, but one Latin phrase may have suggested the waters that Spenser developed allegorically into the Well of Life. On the third day of battle the combatants present themselves as "stagmati," a verb in a variant spelling that could be based on either "stagnum" (pool) or "stannum" (tin or a silver-and-lead alloy). What the two combatants in *DOW* received during the night before had been either bodily refreshment in a pool or the services of a smith to solder their damaged equipment. The idea of a pool to refresh the weary duellers between days of conflict in the heat of that climate may have suggested to Spenser the water into which the Red Cross Knight fell at the end of the first day's fight with the dragon. Spenser also notes on the next morning that the Knight's weapon has been strengthened. Some of Spenser's battle rhetoric suggests that he may have read the Latin text. The battle rhetoric of the three-day combat in *DOW* seems to be echoed in phrases and figures like Canto V.7, "stricken strike and beaten beat"; Canto VI.44, the metaphor of the fighting boars, the torture of breathlessness; Canto XI.42, the hammer beating the anvil. Further, there is an indication that behind the fire-breathing dragon is the metaphor of a full-rigged ship spewing Greek fire. After victory both heroes are honored with triumphal processions and gifts from the grateful inhabitants of Jerusalem/Eden.

Finally there is one clue that Manuscript Faustina B vi, which contains *DOW*, might have been in Ireland in the latter part of the sixteenth century. John Bale's name appears on the verso of folio 37, spelled John Bayle. Perhaps this is an indication that the manuscript was part of the tremendous personal library that Bale collected at the dissolution of the monasteries, although the assorted items now bound as Faustina B vi cannot be identified in the list Bale made of the manuscripts of that collection. Bale had his library with him when he became Bishop of Ossory in Ireland in 1552. A year later, when Queen Mary came to the throne, he was forced to flee to Geneva, leaving his library behind. The library was subsequently scattered in an Irish uprising. Only some forty of his four hundred volumes have since been identified. Further investigation by Bale scholars could clarify whether Faustina B vi ought to be included among these.

The intertextuality of *DOW* and *Sir Gawain and the Green Knight* or of *DOW* and *The Faerie Queene*, Book I, remains to be explored, but behind the resplendent red and gold of Gawain's costume lies the story of how he gained his fame, and behind Spenser's dragon and brazen castle may lie the story of how Gawain fought Greek fire and a Persian champion to preserve Jerusalem for the Christians.

Editorial Policy of This Text and Translation

The single extant manuscript of *De ortu Waluuanii* is contained in the codex British Museum Cotton Faustina B vi, 23r to 38r. Immediately preceding and following are two other works related to the Arthurian legend: *Historia Meriadoci*, 2r to 23r, a romance in Latin prose, and "Britones a troianis duxerunt originem," 38r to 40v, an abridgment of Geoffrey of Monmouth's *Historia Regum Britanniae*. All three works are in the same fourteenth-century hand, undamaged and apparently complete.

Making up the rest of Cotton Faustina B vi, Part 1, are historical materials: annals, lists of kings, a roster of the monks of Croxden, papal letters, the obituary calendar of the Nunnery of Daunton in Kent, records of financial matters for Canterbury Cathedral. Part 2 contains the Middle English poem *Desert of Religion*. The script is

Gothic Textura. The script style approximates that of the scribe of Jacobus de Voragine, *Legenda Sanctorum* (Paris, 1312), as illustrated by S. H. Thomson, *Latin Bookhands of the Later Middle Ages* (Cambridge, 1969). A wide range of abbreviations is used: single letters, shortened words, suprascript letters, and various symbols. Among the decorations are initial letters in red and blue calligraphy. The initials are filled in with spirals and dots. Some of the flourishes descending in the lower margins are cut off by trimming. The capitals within the text are filled in with yellow. Beginning on folio 27, line drawings appear at random in the margins; most are profile caricatures that predate the present binding. Capitalization and punctuation in the manuscript are systematic. Three capitals indicate a new story, two capitals a chapter or paragraph, and a single capital a sentence. The capitalization of proper names varies. The punctuation within the sentence separates main grammatical divisions, but it is not completely consistent. Quoted material may be bracketed in the margin or underlined. Lines of verse are capitalized and identified with the mark of a slashed "v" in the margin.

Working from microfilm and the manuscript itself to prepare the edition, I have attempted to present the text as it is contained in the single manuscript, within the limits of modern printing conventions and punctuation. I have followed the manuscript carefully in regard to sentence division, where Bruce's edition of 1913 does not. Bruce's edition, prepared from a handwritten copy made for him at the British Museum, contains some typographical errors and omissions, which, along with variant readings from his edition, are noted in the apparatus. I have used "j" and "v" for consonantal "i" and "u." I have retained a nonclassical spelling for words that are medieval variants. Paragraph indentations follow the manuscript.

The translation is also conservative. While not quite a word-for-word translation, I have tried to present it sentence by sentence, dividing the sentences into smaller units only when the Latin sentence length becomes unwieldy. Paragraphing in the English follows modern conventions.

A project of this scope is rarely the work of one person alone. I want to thank many friends for their help, particularly Ernest York and Richard Baldes of the University of Alabama, Fr. Thomas Schnurr of Southern Benedictine College, Samuel Pezzillo of Birmingham-Southern College, and Carol D. Lanham of the University of California at Los Angeles. Sumner Willard, Flowers Braswell, and Jonathan Boulton shared significant material from their own research. J. F. Verbruggen, Lynn White, Jr., and Valerie Lagorio have listened to my ideas and offered suggestions. Florence Fitzgibbon, J. August Kling, and William J. Dempsey assisted in the final preparation. I am particularly grateful to editors Lowry Nelson, Jr., and James J. Wilhelm for working with me toward a final draft of the text and translation. My special thanks go to my mother, Marjory Moore Leake, my first Latin teacher, who joined in this project with expertise and unfailing enthusiasm, and to my husband, Jim Houston Day, Sr., whose encouragement made it possible.

Select Bibliography

I. Editions

Bruce, James Douglas, ed. *"De ortu Waluuanii."* *PMLA*, *13* (1898), 365–455.

——, ed. *Historia Meriadoci* and *De ortu Waluuanii.* Hesperia, 2. Göttingen: Dandenhoed & Ruprecht, 1913.

II. Translations

Day, Mildred Leake, trans. "The Rise of Gawain, Nephew of Arthur: Translation and Study of *De Ortu Waluuanii Nepotis Arturi*, a Medieval Latin Prose Romance." Dissertation, University of Alabama (1975).

Wieber, James Leon, trans. "A Translation and Literary Study of *De ortu Walwanii*, a Thirteenth Century Romance." Dissertation, Michigan State University (1974).

III. Criticism and Study Guides

Ancrene Riwle. The English Text, ed. by Frances Mack. EETS, 252. London: Oxford, 1963.

Anderson, R. C. *Oared Fighting Ships*. London: Marshall, 1962. See also his article "Ship" in the *Encyclopaedia Britannica*, 1972.

Bale, John. *Index Britanniae Scriptorum*. Ed. R. L. Poole and M. Bateson. London: Oxford, 1902.

——. *Scriptorum Illustrium Majoris Brytanniae . . . Catalogus*. 2 vols. Basil: Oporium, 1557–59; microcard, Louisville, Ky.: Lost Cause Press, 1959.

xxxix

Biket, Robert. *Lai du Cor.* Ed. H. Dörner. Strasbourg, 1907.

Bromwich, Rachel. *Trioedd Ynys Prydein.* 2nd ed. Cardiff: University of Wales, 1978.

Bruce, James Douglas. *The Evolution of Arthurian Romance from the Beginning down to the Year 1300.* 2 vols. Baltimore: 1928; rpt. Gloucester, Mass.: Peter Smith, 1958.

Brugger, Ernst. "Zu *Historia Meriadoci* und *De Ortu Walwanii.*" *Zeitschrift für französische Sprache und Literatur,* 46 (1923), 247–80, 406–40.

Busby, Keith. *Gauvain in Old French Literature.* Amsterdam: Rodopi, 1980.

Chrétien de Troyes. *Le Roman de Perceval (Le Conte du Graal).* Ed. William Roach. Geneva: Droz. 1956.

Day, Mildred Leake. "Scarlet Surcoat and Gilded Armor: The Literary Tradition of Gawain's Costume in *Sir Gawain and the Green Knight* and *De ortu Waluuanii.*" *Interpretations, 15,* (1984), 53–8.

Epro, Margaret, ed. "The Romance of *Hunbaut*: An Arthurian Poem of the Thirteenth Century." Dissertation, University of Pennsylvania (1975).

Evenhuis, J. R. "Het Grieksevuur." *Spiegel Historiael, 10,* 5 (1975), 298–303.

Ewe, Herbert. *Schiffe auf Siegeln.* Berlin: Delius, Klasing, 1972. Item 37, p. 120.

Frye, Northrop. *The Secular Scripture: A Study of the Structure of Romance.* Cambridge, Mass.: Harvard University Press, 1976.

Galyon, Aubrey, "*De ortu Waluanii* and the Theory of Illumination." *Neophilologus,* 62 (1978), 335–41.

Geoffrey of Monmouth. *Historia Regum Britanniae.* Ed. Acton Griscom. London: Longmans, 1929.

Gout, Paul Émile. *Le Mont-Saint-Michel: Histoire de l'Abbaye et de la Ville.* 2 vols. Paris: Librairie Armand Colin, 1910.

Harward, Vernon J., Jr. *The Dwarfs of Romance and Celtic Tradition.* Leiden: Brill, 1958.

Heinrich von dem Türlin. *Diu Crône.* Ed. G.H.F. Scholl. Amsterdam, 1966.

Henry of Huntingdon. "Letter to Warinus." *Chronique de Robert de Torigni.* Ed. Léopold Delisle. Rouen: Société de l'Histoire de Normandie, 1872–73. I, 97–119.

Hoepffner, Ernst. "The Breton Lais." *Arthurian Literature in the Middle Ages.* Ed. R. S. Loomis. Oxford: Clarendon, 1959. pp. 112–21.

Howlett, Richard, ed. *The Chronicle of Robert of Torigni, Abbot of the Monastery of St. Michael-in-Peril-of-the-Sea.* Chronicles of the Reigns of Stephen, Henry II, and Richard I, Vol. 4. London: Master of the Rolls of Great Britain, 1889.

Itinerarium peregrinorum et gesta regis Ricardi. Ed. W. Stubbs. *Chronicles and Memorials of the Reign of Richard I.* Rolls Series. London, 1864.

Kemp, Peter. *The History of Ships.* New York: Galahad, 1979.

Kittredge, George Lyman. *A Study of Gawain and the Green Knight.* Cambridge, Mass.: Harvard University Press, 1916; rpt. Gloucester, Mass.: Peter Smith, 1960.

Kratz, Bernd. "Die *Crône* Heinrichs von dem Tûrlin und die *Enfances Gauvain.*" *Germanisch-romanische Monatschrift,* 53 (1972), 351–56.

Le Haut Livre du Graal, Perlesvaus. Ed. William Albert Nitze and Thomas Jenkins. Modern Philology Monographs. Chicago: University of Chicago, 1937.

"Les Enfances Gauvain." Ed. Paul Meyer. *Romania,* 39 (1910), 1–32.

Loomis, Roger Sherman. *Celtic Myth and Arthurian Romance.* New York: Columbia University Press, 1927.

———. "The Latin Romances." *Arthurian Literature in the Middle Ages.* Oxford: Clarendon, 1959. Pp. 472–79.

———. "More Celtic Elements in 'Gawain and the Green Knight.'" *Journal of English and German Philology,* 42 (1943), 149–84; rpt. *Studies in Medieval Literature: A Memorial Collection of Essays* by R. S. Loomis. Ed. Dorothy Bethurum Loomis. New York: Burt Franklin, 1970. Pp. 157–92.

———. "Scotland and the Arthurian Legend." *Proceedings of the Society of Antiquaries of Scotland,* 89 (1955–56); rpt. *Studies in Medieval Literature.* Ed. D. B. Loomis. New York: Burt Franklin, 1970. Pp. 135–55.

Mappae Clavicula. Eds. Cyril Stanley Smith and John G. Hawthorne. *Transactions of the American Philosophical Society,* N.S. 64 (1974).

Markman, Alan M. "Sir Gawain of Britain: A Study of the Romance Elements." Dissertation, University of Michigan (1955).

Mills, Maldwyn, ed. *Lybeaus Desconus*. Early English Text Society, 261. London: Oxford, 1969.

Morriss, Margaret Shove. "The Authorship of the *De ortu Waluuanii* and the *Historia Meriadoci*." *PMLA*, 23 (1908), 599–645.

Mullen, William B. "A Critical Study of the *Historia Meriadoci*." Dissertation, Columbia (1951).

Newstead, Helaine. "The Besieged Ladies in Arthurian Romance." *PMLA*, 33 (1948), 803–30.

Partington, J. R. *A History of Greek Fire and Gunpowder*. Cambridge: Heffer, 1960.

Propp, Vladimir. *Morphology of the Folktale*. 2nd ed. Austin: University of Texas Press, 1968.

Rajna, Pio. "Per le origini e la storia primitiva del Ciclo brettone." *Studii Medievali*, 3 (1930), 201–57.

———. "Sono il *De ortu Waluuanii* e l'*Historia Meriadoci* Opera de un Medesimo Autore?" *Medieval Studies in Memory of Gertrude Schoepperle Loomis*. Ed. R. S. Loomis. Paris: Champion, 1927. Pp. 1–20.

Rank, Otto. *The Myth of the Birth of the Hero*. Ed. Philip Freund. Nervous and Mental Diseases Monographs. New York, 1959.

Sir Gawain and the Grene Gome. Ed. R. T. Jones. New York: Barnes & Noble, 1972.

Smail, R. C. *Crusading Warfare (1097–1193)*. Cambridge: Cambridge University Press, 1956.

Socrates. *Historia Ecclesiastica*, 7.18. *Patrologia Graeca*, 67: col. 778.

Spenser, Edmund. *The Faerie Queene, Books I and II*. Eds. Robert Kellogg and Oliver Steele. New York: Odyssey, 1965.

Stones, Edward L. G., ed. *Anglo-Scottish Relations 1174–1328*. Oxford: Clarendon, 1965.

Theophilus. *De Diversis Artibus*. Tr. C. R. Dodwell. London: Nelson, 1961.

Thompson, Raymond H. "Gawain Against Arthur: The Impact of a Mythological Pattern upon Arthurian Tradition in Accounts of the Birth of Gawain." *Folklore*, 85 (1974), 113–21.

————. "The Perils of Good Advice: The Effect of the Wise Counsellor upon the Conduct of Gawain." *Folklore*, 90 (1979), 71–76.

The Turk and Gawain. Eds. J. W. Hales and F. J. Furnivall. *Bishop Percy's Manuscript*. London, 1867–68. I, 88–102.

Unger, Richard. *The Ship in Medieval Economy, 600–1600*. London: Croom Helm, 1980.

Vegetius. *Epitoma Rei Militaris*. Ed. Charles Lang. Leipzig: Teubner, 1868.

Verbruggen, J. R. *The Art of Warfare in Western Europe during the Middle Ages from the Eighth Century to 1340*. Trans. Sumner Willard and S.C.M. Southern. Amsterdam: North-Holland, 1977.

The Rise of Gawain, Nephew of Arthur

DE ORTU WALUUANII NEPOTIS ARTURI

[Cotton Faustina B vi, fol.23r, col.2] Uterpendragon
Rex, pater Arturi, omnium Britannie confinium provinciarum sue
dicioni reges subegerat; tributariosque efficiens, eorum filios
partim loco obsidum, partim honestate morum militarique
erudiendos disciplina, sua in curia detinebat. Inter quos Loth   5
nepos Sichelmi regis Norgwegie educabatur, adolescens mirandus
aspectu robore corporis animique virtute preditus, unde et regi
Uthero eiusque filio Arturo ceteris suis coetaneis karior
habitus, ipsius secreta cubiculi continue frequentabat. Erat
autem regi filia Anna dicta incomparabilis pulcritudinis que cum   10
matre regina in thalamo morabatur. Cum qua dum predictus
adolescens sepe juveniliter luderet et jocosa secretius verba
consereret, utrique alterutro capiuntur amore. Alterni tamen
affectus diu ab invicem cum timore tum pudore dissimulati
sunt. Verum quia ad instar flamme amor quo magis tegitur: 15
eo magis accenditur indeque capit augmentum, unde minui
festinatur; magnitudinem tandem amoris in se continere non
valentes, que mente conceperant mutuo patefaciunt. Sui igitur
voti compotes effecti, assensum voluptati adhibent; statimque
illa impregnata intumuit.   [23v,col.1]   Pariendi vero   20
appropinquante termino, egritudinem simulans, secreto cubat
cubiculo, unam tantum pedissequam huius rei habens consciam.

---

6. Sichelmi: chelmi MS; Sichelini, Bruce (cf. Geof. Historia 9.11)
adolescens: adoloscens MS, Bruce 12. sepe: added above line in MS.
15-16. cf. Ovid. Meta. 4.1.64; bracketed in MS.

2

THE RISE OF GAWAIN, NEPHEW OF ARTHUR

King Uther Pendragon, father of Arthur, subjugated the kings of all the provinces bordering Britannia to his authority; in order to insure their subjection he held their sons in his court, partly in the position of hostages, partly to be trained in nobility of conduct and military discipline. 5 Among these hostages was Loth, nephew of Sichelm, King of Norway, a young man of striking appearance, strong of body and manly of spirit. For these qualities he was held in higher esteem than others of his age by Uther and his son Arthur, and he frequently visited in their private living quarters. The 10 king also had a daughter named Anna, an incomparable beauty, who still lived with her mother the queen in her chambers. As Loth would often tease her playfully and engage in merry words with her quite privately, they were both seized with love for one another. Yet for a long time, from shyness and shame, their 15 mutual affections were hidden from each other. Truly, "love is like a flame, the more it is concealed the hotter it burns," and from hasty suppression it becomes intensified. Not being able to contain within themselves so great a love, they revealed to one another what possessed their hearts. With both their 20 prayers answered, they yielded to their desires, and soon Anna conceived a child. When she was near term carrying the child, she feigned illness and retired to a private bedchamber, with only her lady-in-waiting knowing why.

---

*Asterisks indicate that further information is provided in the Textual Notes at the end.

3

Tempus tandem quo fetum expelleret advenerat, parvulumque
eleganti forma enixa est. Conduxerat autem ditissimos e
transmarinis finibus commercia sectantes, pactaque cum eis sub
jurejurando fuerat ut statim ubi in lucem prodiret, ne a quoquam
comperiretur, secum suam in patriam infantem abducerent; ac   5
usque adultam etatem diligenter educarent. Natum itaque
infantulum, nemine sciente, negociatores suscipiunt, cum quo
genitrix eis auri et argenti preciosarumque vestium
innumerabilem copiam contulit. Tradidit quoque ingentis precii
pallium, insertis gemmis auro undique intextum, necnon et anulum   10
lapide smaragdino insignitum, quem a rege custodiendum acceperat
quo ipse dum taxat festivis diebus uti solebat. Cartam eciam
regis sigillo signatam addidit, cuius textus eum certis
insinuabat indiciis ex regis Norwegie nepote sororeque Arturi
progenitum Waluuaniumque a genitrice nominatum; et propter regis   15
timorem ad extraneas fuisse destinatum provincias. Hec ideo
illa, scilicet pallium, anulum, et cartam, provido usa consilio
cum eo prebere studuit, ut si forte quandoque rediens a
parentibus [23v,col.2] non agnitus refutaretur, signum
certitudinis exhiberent; et per eorum indicia ad parentum   20
perveniret noticiam.

Negociatores igitur sue tuicioni commissum parvulum tollentes
navem conscendunt; datisque ventis carbasis, alta sulcantes
equora viii tandem die Gallicanas allabuntur ad horas, nactique
continentem duobus miliariis a civitate Narbonensi appulsi sunt. 25

---

10. intextum: in textum MS, Bruce   23. conscendunt: concendunt MS,
Bruce   24. allabuntur: albabuntur MS, Bruce.

4

At last the time came for the delivery of the infant, and she gave birth to a male child of rare beauty. Earlier, Anna had made a contract with certain wealthy men who had come from beyond the seas seeking trade, and she confirmed the pact with them under oath that as soon as the infant had come into the world, lest anyone should find out, they would carry the child away into their own land and bring it up with care. So with no one knowing of the child's birth, the merchants accepted the infant son along with an untold wealth of gold, silver, and rich vestments that the mother had provided. In addition, she entrusted to them an immensely valuable pallium* embroidered with jewels worked in gold over its entire surface, as well as the signet ring set with an emerald that she had received in trust from the king, a ring which he himself was accustomed to wear only on feast days. She added also a document impressed with the king's seal, the text of which identified with irrefutable proofs that the child, whom she had named Gawain, was the son of the nephew of the King of Norway and of the sister of Arthur; the document explained further that he had been sent to a foreign land out of fear of the king. Thus these items—the pallium, the ring, and the document—she wanted the child to have, foreseeing that whenever he returned, if it happened that he was not recognized by his parents and they rejected him, these would display proof of his identity, and through their evidence he would attain the acknowledgment of his parents.

The merchants, accordingly, boarded ship carrying the infant committed to them for fostering. Hoisting the canvas to the winds and plowing a wake across the sea, at last on the eighth day they were sailing toward the coast of Gaul, and reaching shore, they came to land two miles from the city of Narbonne.*

Quo ubi applicuerunt, sale reumateque maris tabentes, ad urbem
se spaciatum, lintre in portu relicto, omnes properant, unum
tantummodo puerum qui suas res lactentemque in cunis jactentem
tueretur deserentes. Remocius quippe ab urbe sub prerupta rupe
appulerant, nullumque interim ratem aditurum credebant. Sed   5
illis egressis, forte quidam piscator e vicino pago, Viamundus
vocabulo, rebus quidem pauper sed genere et moribus honestus,
ut moris cotidie habebat cum conjuge per litus gradiebatur,
investigans si piscem invenire potuisset freti retractu in
continenti destitutum cuius sibi precio victum adquireret. Hic   10
carinam appulsam intuitus, ceteris omissis, illuc confestim
tetendit,   ingressusque neminem excepto puero qui ad eius
tutelam relictus fuerat, et illum quidem dormientem repperit.
Videns autem parvulum prestanti forma, navemque sine custode
omnibus refertam diviciis suamque considerans paupertatem, quam   15
ibi   for[24r,col.1]tuna favente relevare poterat   (ut in
proverbio dicitur, "oportunitas loci et temporis reddit
latronem"), quicquid majoris estimacionis in auro et argento
variaque suppellectili sibi videbatur diripuit. Infantem
quoque et thecam ad capud eius stantem in qua pallium,   20
anulus et carta continebantur uxori tradens, opibus honusti
ad sua cum festinacione, nullo negocium advertente,
abscesserunt. Institores autem post paululum ad navalia
regressi dampnum sibi illatum rebus sublatis offendunt.

---

1. cf. Verg. A. 1.173.   3. in cunis: incunis, MS
17. bracketed in MS.

6

From here, once they had heaved to, all the men, dripping
salt and sea water, hastened on foot to the city, leaving the
ship in port with only a single serving boy to look after their
merchandise and the nursling in the cradle. Actually, they had
steered under a steep cliff quite a distance from the city and   5
thought that no one would come near the ship in the meantime.
But after they had gone, by chance a certain fisherman from the
neighboring region who was called Viamundus (a man poor in
possessions but noble by birth and bearing) came walking along
the shore with his wife as was his daily routine, searching if   10
he might find a fish stranded at the shore by the ebb of the
sea, for the price of which he would buy food. When he saw the
keel drawn to shore, abandoning the other effort, he at once set
out in that direction. On boarding, he found that no one except
a boy had been left to guard it and, what is more, he was   15
asleep. Seeing an infant of such beauty and an unguarded ship
filled with all riches, and considering his own poverty which
here, fortune favoring, he would be able to relieve (as the
proverb says, "opportunity of place and time makes the thief"),
he plundered whatever seemed to him of greatest value in silver   20
and gold and various furnishings. He handed the infant to his
wife as well as the coffer placed at his head that contained the
pallium, the ring and the document. Laden with riches, they
escaped quickly to their dwelling, the affair being observed by
no one.   25

   The merchants, though, when they returned later to the
mooring place, discovered the theft of their property.

Cuius rei eventu inopino dolore perculsi, maximoque merore
consternati ad gemitus et fletus omnes conversi sunt; diemque in
lamentacionem continuaverunt et maxime ob infantis surrepcionem
quem sue fidei constabat creditum. Moxque ad hoc idoneos
electos per vicina lictora ruraque nuncios mittunt, qui rem   5
diligentur indagarent et qui sibi tantum intulissent discrimen
inquirerent. Sed quoniam "quod omnium latet noticiam difficile
deprehenditur," nichil certitudinis anticipantes ad navem qui
missi fuerant mesti remearunt.

Viamundus autem subtractam cum infantulo substanciam ad   10
casam deferens occuluit; ipsumque loco filii quia proprio
carebat, adhibita diligencia enutrivit. Verebatur tamen opulen-
ciam qua pollebat in palam proferre quia et egestas qua hactenus
afficiebatur exstabat notissima, et furti quod commiserat adhuc
fiebat questio; ne opum ostentacione, perpetrati sceleris   15
infamia notaretur. [24r,col.2] Septem autem annorum transcurso
spacio, Romam pergere deliberavit et facti penitudine ductus; et
quod non dubitabat se illo ut in extranea regione suis faculta-
tibus licite posse uti. Omnibus igitur vie necessariis paratis
et compositis, uxore filio adoptivo, familiaque comitantibus cum   20
universa substancia iter arripuit; inque brevi sane et prospere
Romana menia attigit. Ingressus autem omni die urbem circumqua-
que circumibat, cunctaque perscrutans; statum loci mores
civium et nomina senatorum ac principum callide inquirebat.

7-8. bracketed in MS. 24. senatorum: sanatorum MS, Bruce
principum: principium MS, Bruce

They were shocked by the unexpected turn of events, and overwhelmed by the great loss, they began weeping and groaning. They continued all day in deep despair, particularly for the kidnapped infant who had been entrusted to their safekeeping. In a short time they sent carefully chosen agents through the neighboring shores and fields to investigate the matter thoroughly and find out who had inflicted such a loss on them. But since "that which lies hidden from the knowledge of all is with difficulty discovered," those who had been sent returned sadly to the ship without having discovered any trace of the infant or the treasure.

Viamundus, meanwhile, hid the stolen wealth that he had carried to his cottage along with the infant boy. He cared for the child, exerting all concern as if he were his son as he had none of his own. He feared to reveal the riches which he now had in his control, lest by ostentatious display the ugly truth of the crime he had perpetrated would become known, because not only was the poverty which had burdened him up to this time most obvious, but also the inquest into the theft which he had committed was still in progress.

After a period of seven years had elapsed, he decided to make a pilgrimage to Rome, led both by repentance for his deed and by the fact that he did not doubt he would be able to use his abundance without fear of the law in a region where he was not known. When everything necessary for the journey had been prepared and assembled, he set out with his wife and adopted son, his household accompanying him with all his possessions. By good fortune he arrived in a short time safely at the walls of Rome. When he entered, however, he walked about the city all day through every section and scrutinized the entire area. He shrewdly inquired about the conditions of the place, the customs of the citizens, and the names of the senators and most distinguished men.

9

Roma vero ea tempestate vi barbarorum capta et subacta fuerat et
pene usque ad internicionem desolata, muris dirutis, edificiis
combustis, civibus captivatis et dispersis variisque suppliciis
interemptis. Sed novus in imperio imperator successerat, qui
ruine urbis condolens, diruta reedificabat, cives dispersos   5
congregabat, captos redimebat summopere dans operam, eam ad
pristine felicitatis statum reducere. Quibus Viamundus agnitis
et, ut erat astuti ingenii, rem sibi intelligens ad votum
succedere, nil moratus se egregio cultu adornavit, servos et
quam plurima mancipia a vicinis oppidis, magnosque apparatus   10
comparavit. Servorumque numerosa turba vallatus, per mediam
urbem ad palacium tendit, omnibus spectaculo factus, cum ex
splendidis ornamentis, tum ex se stipancium multitudine.
Veniensque [24v,col.1] ad imperatorem, honorifice suscipitur.
Cum quo demum colloquia conserens, se ex nobilissima Romanorum   15
oriundum familia, Gallieque partibus commoratum populi ducatum
habuisse, sed audita urbis clade et infortunio se concivium
vires ad auctum illo properasse, utque sibi cum suis habitandi
in ea locum tribueret suppliciter flagitabat. Imperator autem
eum non parve generositatis, cum ex veneranda canicie, cum   20
variarum decore rerum, tum et satellitum numerositate estimans
et consciens, quod ad se venerit gracias agit seque eum
si in urbe commoraretur multiplici donaturum spondet honore.

---

6. congregabat: cogregabat MS, Bruce 11. comparavit: compar[a]vit
MS. 15. conserens MS: conserens [narravit], Bruce. 20. canicie:
canrcie MS, Bruce. 22. consciens: comciens MS; coniciens, Bruce.

In fact, Rome at this period had been captured by the might of the barbarians and sacked, ravaged almost to the point of utter destruction—walls thrown down, buildings burned, and citizens captured, driven out, and slain by various means of torture. But a new emperor had succeeded to the empire who, grieving over the ruin of the city, was rebuilding the destroyed sections, gathering together the scattered citizens, redeeming the captives, striving with utmost diligence to bring Rome back to her former condition of felicity. Viamundus, perceiving this and, as he was astute by nature, comprehending the situation to be favorable to his own goals, without delay dressed himself in distinguished style and acquired servants and as many slaves as possible from the neighboring towns, fitting them out magnificently. Escorted by a numerous train of servants, he proceeded through the center of the city to the palace, creating a spectacle for all to behold not only with the splendid trappings but also with the size of his retinue. Coming before the emperor, he was received with honor. When at last he had the opportunity of speaking with the emperor, Viamundus presented in his petition that he had come from a most noble family of Romans and had been military leader of the people of a region of Gaul until he heard of the destruction and misfortune of the city of Rome and hastened there to swell the ranks of his fellow citizens, and he begged the emperor to allot a place in the city for him and his people to live together. The emperor, assessing him and judging him to be of no minor nobility not only from his venerable gray hair and the elegance of his manifold possessions, but also from his numerous followers, gave thanks because he had come to him and promised that if he remained in the city he would endow him with many honors.

Deditque illi aulam marmoream mire structure stupendisque
comptam edificiis pre foribus sui palacii, que Scipionis
Affricani testatur fuisse. Municipia quoque vineas et
agriculturas extra urbem contulit, suis servituras expensis.
Tante itaque fortune Viamundus ultra omnem estimacionem   5
nactus beneficia, se tam lepide, tamque decenter et generose
agebat, ut imperatorem, senatum populumque in sui admiracionem
converteret; omniumque se amatum traheret affectus, celebrisque
sermo de sua largitate et munificencia per totam urbem clam
palamque ferreretur. Senatorum quippe et nobilium Rome ad eum   10
cotidie conventus fiebat, nec non et ab aula imperiali
pretextati pueri, militumque turba ob graciam parvuli
confluebant [24v,col.2] quos variis deliciis, oppiparatis
conviviis, donisque honorabat largissimis. Crescente interea
etate puero, crescebat et animi virtute et corporis habilitate,   15
suique genitoris qui credebatur emulator existens; industrie,
facecie probitatique studebat. Frequentabat et ipse palacium
familiarisque cum subditis habebatur principi. Quedam enim in
illo ingenite vigebant virtutes, quibus se videncium animos ad
se amandum extorquebat et alliciebat. Erat siquidem procera   20
decentique statura, lepido gestu, pulcra facie, ingentique
preditus fortitudine. Jamque xii^{um} evi annum attigerat, cum
Viamundus gravi tentus egritudine lecto decubuit. Qui
ingravescente languore, dum sibi vite finem imminere
cerneret; per primores civitatis imperatorem papamque   25
(Sulpicium per id tempus apostolice sedi presidentem) ut
ad se venire, suaque colloquia dignarentur plurimum exorabat.

---

12. pretaxtati: pretexati MS, Bruce 13. oppiparatis: opperipatis
MS; oppipatus, Bruce 19. virtutes: virtutis MS, Bruce

And he gave him a marble residence of remarkably good design set
about with impressive buildings, located in front of the gates
of his own palace, a hall attested to have belonged to Scipio
Africanus. The emperor also conferred on him towns, vineyards,
and fields outside the city which were to provide for his   5
expenses.*

    Thus Viamundus, having obtained favors of such good
fortune beyond all estimation, conducted himself so fitly and
nobly and with such charm that he earned the admiration of the
emperor, senate, and people and drew all hearts to love him; and   10
the oft-repeated story of his lavishness and generosity spread
privately and publicly throughout the city. Daily the senators
and nobles of Rome gathered about him, and not only these men,
but out of regard for his young lad, boys wearing the toga
praetexta of noble birth and a number of knights came from the   15
imperial court, all of whom Viamundus honored with many
delicacies, sumptuous banquets and rich gifts. Meanwhile, as
the boy grew, he increased both in manliness of spirit and
discipline of body; and he strove purposefully after courtesy
and prowess, emerging as the image of his supposed father. He   20
frequented the palace and was considered a friend to the emperor
and to those under him. Truly something of excellence
flourished naturally in that young man wherewith he ravished the
hearts of the perceptive and drew them to love him. He had tall
and noble stature, graceful bearing, and a handsome face, and he   25
was endowed with remarkable strength.

    When the boy had reached his twelfth year, Viamundus took
to his bed, stricken with serious illness. Then because of
increasing weakness he realized the end of his life was
imminent; and he begged earnestly through the leaders of the   30
city that the emperor and the pope--Sulpicius occupying at that
time the papal throne--should come to him and hear his words.

Illi autem tanti viri preces quem ob morum liberalitatem non parum dilexerant minime renuentes, assumptis secum viris excellencioribus civitatis gravato affectu ad eum convenere. Advenientibus vero Viamundus primum de impertitis sibi ab illis beneficiis debitas grates exsoluit; deinde eos secreto 5 convocans, vite prioris statum quo casu tantarum diviciarum gloriam adeptus fuerit puerumque quem educabat reppererit, totiusque vite ordinem seriatim exposuit. Subiunxitque, "Hoc estuanti," inquit, "animo vestre [25r, col.1] celsitudini sepius intimare deliberavi sed semper temporis oportunitatem 10 opperiens; usque ad presens distuli. Nunc autem ultimo fato incumbente ea fateri compulsus; licet quod postulo homini servilis condicionis a tocius orbis dominis juste regari possit, tamen amicicie familiaritatisque memores quibus me dignati estis mee vos peticioni non abnuere estimo. Est quidem quod vos 15 petiturus accivi hunc puerum quem loco filii enutrivi, et cum quo hec omnis mihi rerum copia contigit, vestre sullimitatis tuicioni committere, ut eum educantes ad militarem ordinem dum etas affuerit promoveatis. Nepotem quippe Arturi regis Britannie (iam enim patre defuncto susceperat), de quo tante 20 probitatis fama ubique volat eum esse noveritis, quem apparentem nobilitate non degeneraturum non dubito. Rem tamen ab omnibus et ab ipso laudo haberi secretam, nec eciam nomen ipsius donec a suis cognoscatur parentibus patefiat, quia et hoc carte monimenta que eius testantur prosapiam prohibent. 25

---

2. dilexerant: dilexerat MS, Bruce 3. gravato: gravito MS; grauuido, Bruce 8. totiusque: totisque corrected to totiusque in MS. 13. regari MS: negari, Bruce 20. defuncto MS: defuncto [regnum], Bruce 22. apparentem: apparentum MS; a parentum, Bruce degeneraturum: degneraturum MS, Bruce

Those men, not wishing to spurn the entreaties of so great a man
whom they esteemed so much because of his generous character
came bringing with them high-ranking men of the city and
gathered before him with heavy hearts. Viamundus first gave
thanks to those present for the benefits they had shared with   5
him; then consulting with them in private, he revealed the state
of his former life, by what chance he had obtained the
magnificence of such great wealth and the boy whom he had raised
as a son; and he laid bare the tenor of his whole life in proper
order.   10

      He concluded, "I resolved so often with a burning desire
to reveal this to your highnesses; but I delayed, always
awaiting the opportune moment; I put it off till the present.
Now, however, since my ultimate fate is imminent, I am compelled
to confess these things. Though what I ask may be summarily   15
adjudicated for a man of my lowly estate by the masters of the
entire world, still I reckon that you, remembering the friendship and fellowship by which you have honored me, will not deny
my petition. It is specifically for this matter that I summoned
you: to commit to the protection of your highnesses this boy   20
whom I have nurtured as a son and with whom all this abundance
of material things fell to my lot, so that you may advance him,
educating him for the order of knighthood when he comes of age.
From the proof I will give you, you will learn that he is the
nephew of Arthur, King of Britannia (by this time, Uther being   25
deceased, Arthur had succeeded), the man whose fame for great
prowess flies everywhere; I do not doubt that this boy,
outstanding in nobility, will maintain this quality without
dishonor. I recommend, nevertheless, that the matter be held
secret from all men and from the boy himself; don't let even his   30
name be revealed until he is acknowledged by his parents because
the terms of the document that attests his origin prohibit it.

15

Ubi autem in virilem etatem proruperit, cum vestris litteris, et
sue propaginis certis indiciis, que satis apud me habentur
probabilia, oro remittatur." Puerumque advocans qui quia quo
nomine censeretur nesciebatur usque ad illud tempus, puer sine
nomine vocatus fuerat, imperatoris amplexus vestigia supplici   5
prece summisque votis, eum commendavit. Loculum quoque quo
testamenta a matre contradita continebantur jubens afferri
imperatori ostendit. Quibus [25r,col.2] visis imperator viri
liberalitatem circa puerum habitam multa laude efferens, puerum
injectis brachiis suscipit, se eius voluntati per omnia   10
satisfacturum spondens. Sicque Viamundus quod maxime
affectaverat pro voto adeptus, imperatore assidente letus
defungitur; maximaque lamentacione cunctorum in monumentis
nobilium constructa desuper ab imperatore miri operis piramide
sepelitur.   15

Post Viamundi autem obitum puer sine nomine ad palacium
jussu principis ductus, inter regales pueros annumeratur. Trium
vero annorum emenso termino, xv scilicet etatis anno, sua
probitate exigente, armis ab imperatore instruitur. Cum quo et
xx alios juvenes ob graciam ipsius milicia donavit. Indeque cum   20
ceteris tironibus juventuque Romana ad Circum quo cursus equorum
fieri solebant progressus, quanta se ea die virtute egerit, quam
strenue gesserit, favor omnium Circo astancium eum prosecutus
testimonio fuit. In illo siquidem spectaculo nullus ei
resistere, nullus eius viribus equiparari valuit; quin   25
quemcumque obvium haberet mutuo congressu prosterneret.

---

13. in monumentis: monumentis MS, Bruce 25. nullus eius viribus:
in margin in scribe's hand; viribus duplicated in MS. 26. congressu:
congressi MS, Bruce.

16

But when he comes to manhood, I pray let him be sent back with your letter and the sure evidence of his lineage which I consider quite acceptable." And summoning the boy, who until that time had been called "Boy with no Name" because it was not known by what family name he should be registered, he embraced 5 the feet of the emperor and commended the boy to his care with humble pleas and deepest vows. Ordering the coffer which contained the proofs assembled by his mother to be brought out, he presented it to the emperor.

When the emperor had inspected it, he praised the man's 10 generosity toward his foster son, and he accepted the boy, throwing his arms around him and promising that he would fulfill Viamundus' desire in all respects. Thus Viamundus, having achieved to his satisfaction what he had striven for so intensely, with the emperor sitting by his bedside, died happy. 15 With great mourning of all the people, he was buried among the tombs of the nobility in a monument of marvelous workmanship erected by the emperor for his grave.

So it was that after the death of Viamundus the nameless 20 boy was conducted to the palace by order of the emperor and included among the royal children. When three years had passed--that is to say when the boy reached fifteen--and his prowess met the test, he was granted arms by the emperor. As a mark of favor, the emperor also granted arms to twenty other 25 young men in military training with him. Then from the palace with the other new knights and young Romans still in training they proceeded to the Circus where the coursing* of the horses was customarily practiced. On this day so great was the valor with which the new knight conducted himself, so vigorous 30 his exploits, that the cheers of all the people present in the Circus went with him as testimony. No one in that spectacle could withstand him, no one match his strength; in truth whomsoever he encountered in single combat he would overthrow.

17

Qua propter equiriis celebratis, aurea quam rex victori proposuerat insignitus corona, pompa cum laudibus eum prosequente in presencia imperatoris adducitur. Quem imperator de singulari probitate non mediocriter collaudans cuiuscumque [25v,col.1] muneris a se voluisse remuneracionem poscere 5 concessit. Ille autem, "Nil aliud," ait, "tuam mihi, O Imperator, munificenciam opto conferre, nisi ut primam congressionem singularis pugne, que tibi contra tuorum aliquem hostium sit agenda concedat." Annuit imperator eumque in primo equestrium constituit ordine. Prima vero die qua ipse ad 10 miliciam assumptus fuerat, tunicam sibi paraverat purpuream, quam ad pretaxatum equestre certamen processurus armis superinducens; tunicam armature nuncupavit. Dumque a militibus quereretur cur eam super arma induisset, neque enim antea huiusmodi tunica armis septus aliquis usus fuerat, respondit se 15 tunicam armature ad hornatum adhibuisse. Ad quod responsum ei ab omni acclamatur excercitu, "Novus miles cum tunica armature, novus miles cum tunica armature"; ac deinceps hoc illi mansit vocabulum, Miles cum tunica armature. Qui altiori ab imperatore promotus honore semper ad altiora virtutis et probitatis 20 tendebat; cui in omni congressu in omni certamine, celebre nomen singularisque fortitudo ascribebantur.

---

3. presencia MS: presenciam, Bruce 4. cuiuscumque: cuiuscumque mu MS 8. singularis: sigularis MS, Bruce 13. nuncupavit: nunccupavit MS, Bruce 19. altiori: alteriori MS, Bruce 20. altiora: alteriora MS, Bruce

So at the festival of Equirria,* the new knight, wearing
the golden circlet which the emperor had promised to the victor,
was led into the emperor's presence, a cheering procession of
people escorting him. The emperor, praising him in no small way
for his outstanding prowess, granted him the boon of any reward   5
that he would ask of him.

But the young man replied, "I desire nothing of your
bounty, O Emperor, to be bestowed on me, unless it be that I may
undertake the first contest of single combat that you must wage   10
against your enemies."

The emperor assented and placed him in the first order of
equestrians.* On the day when he had received his knighthood,
before he had gone out to the combat on horseback, he arrayed
himself with a crimson tunic to cover his armor. He called it a   15
"surcoat for armor." When asked by the knights why he had put
it on over his armor—and no one before his time had worn a
tunic while dressed in armor—he replied that he had put the
tunic over his armor as splendid attire.

After that reply, all the men acclaimed him, "New knight
with the surcoat for his armor, New knight with the surcoat for
his armor"; and after that the soubriquet "Knight of the
Surcoat" remained his name.

This man who had been advanced by the emperor to very high   25
honor strove always toward even higher achievements in valor
and prowess; a distinguished reputation and singular daring were
attributed to him in every encounter of every tournament.

19

Dum hec Rome geruntur, bellum inter Persarum regem
Christianosque Jerosolimis commorantes oriri contigit.
Ventumque erat ad diem prefinitum certamini et tam equestrium
quam pedestrium ingentibus copiis conferte circumstantes acies,
sibi spectaculum incuciebant terroris; distinctisque ordinibus   5
gradatim [25v,col.2] ad prelium appropiabant. Jamque tubis
clangentibus, tensis nervis, telisque erectis, primipilares
dextras conserere festinabant; dum evo consilioque maturiores
utriusque partis, considerantes tante multitudinis, tantique
roboris conflictum non sine maximo posse fore discrimine, in   10
medium procedentes primum refrenant impetum, ac de pacis
condicione locuturos ad invicem legatos dirigunt. Diutius autem
inter eos locucione habita tandem in hoc universi dedere
consensum: ut hinc et inde unus ad duellum eligeretur et cui
cessisset victoria cederet et rerum unde agebatur dominium.   15
Verumptamen Jerosolomitani quia hoc sine assensu cesaris sub
cuius degebant imperio non audebant concedere, sibi dari
pacierunt inducias donec ad cesarem super hac re legacionem
mitterent et eius voluntatem agnoscerent. Se vero ad hanc
paccionem pronos animo si ab eo concederetur, jurejurando   20
asserebant. Igitur concessis induciis qui hac legacione
fungerentur eligunt, electosque postposita dilacione mittunt.

---

6. appropiabant MS: appropriabant, Bruce   16. Jerosolomitani:
Jerosolitani MS, Bruce 18. pacierunt MS (a variant form of the
verb paciscor): pecierunt, Bruce

While this was going on in Rome, war broke out between the King of Persia and the Christians remaining in Jerusalem. When the day came for battle, the besieging formations of both cavalry and foot drawn up compactly into an enormous force produced thereby a spectacle of terror, and by separate ranks in proper order they drew near to battle. Already the trumpets were being sounded, the bowstrings tautened, the lances couched, and the chief centurions were impatient to join in hand-to-hand combat,* yet at this moment those more mature in both age and wisdom on both sides were meeting in council. When these men considered that the clash of such great multitudes and such great force could not take place without the greatest disaster, they proceeded between the lines, restrained the first attack, and then sent officials to discuss the conditions of peace with each side. After talks between them had been going on for some time, all parties agreed to this: from each side one man should be chosen to duel and victory would go to the man to whom the other yielded, as would the final decision on those matters over which the war had broken out. But because the Jerusalemites did not dare agree without the assent of the emperor under whose rule they lived, they bound themselves to a truce to be granted them until they could send a delegation to the emperor about this matter and ascertain his will. They swore an oath that they agreed in principle to this procedure if it were affirmed by him. Therefore, when the truce had been granted, they selected those who were to act as delegates, and without delay they sent them on the way.

Precipientes illis ut si cesarem quod postulabant minime renuere animadverterent, eciam ad propositum certamen idoneum virum ab eo flagitarent. Missi itaque iter maturantes ad imperatorem veniunt, inductique senatum vie causam disertissime peroraverunt. Imperator autem super relatis inito consilio, 5 eorum peticioni concedendum deliberavit, sed quem cum eis dirigeret dubitabat. Dumque variis sentenciis sermo intractaretur, res [26r,col.1] Militis cum tunica armature defertur ad aures. Qui, nil moratus, in conspectu imperatoris sumpta audacia prorupit, atque, "O," ait, "Imperator, tue 10 munificencie te opto memorem, qua me ad tyrocinium delectum me petente dignanter donasti, ut primum singulare certamen quod tibi tuos contra adversarios ineundum foret mihi annueres. Ecce non tantum tibi et Romano populo verum eciam fidei Christiane a perfidis bellum indicitur; oro tuam sullimitatem ut mihi quod 15 concessit permittat, quatinus et tue sponsionis effectum assequar, et Romani populi dignitatem cultumque religionis ulciscar." Imperator autem licet tam probum militem et sibi necessarium a se dimittere, et tanto destinare discrimini admodum egre ferret, tamen quia sua hoc exigebat promissio, et 20 illo ad tale negocium magis nesciebat idoneum, presertim cum ex illius qui mittendus erat fortitudine suorum omnium vires virtutemque pensandas, seque dampnum et dedecus si vinceretur, lucrum autem et gloriam si vicisset, manere noverat; ex senatusconsultu fieri adjudicavit. 25

---

4. inductique senatum MS: inductique in senatum, Bruce 6. eis: eius MS, Bruce 11. memorem MS: memorem esse, Bruce 15. mihi: added above the line MS.

When instructing these men, they emphasized that if the emperor did not deny their petition, they were also to entreat him earnestly for a man capable of the proposed duel. The emissaries made a hurried journey to the emperor, and when they were brought into the senate, they explained in their most eloquent manner the reason they had come. The emperor, however, after taking counsel concerning their pleas, considered agreeing to their petition but was undecided about whom he should send on their behalf. When the talk had dragged on in a diversity of opinions, the substance of it reached the ears of the Knight of the Surcoat.

Without delay, he took courage and burst into the presence of the emperor, exclaiming, "O Emperor, I wish you to remember the boon you so graciously bestowed on me at the arming of the new knights when you promised me the first single combat that must be undertaken for you against your enemies. Now war is declared by the infidels not only against you and the Roman people, but indeed against the Christian faith. I entreat Your Highness that you now allow what you granted to me, so that I may not only receive your promised boon but may also avenge the honor of the Roman people and the practice of religion."

Although it required parting with so excellent a knight, his own ward, and assigning him to such a duel, yet because fulfilling his promise compelled it and because he knew no better man for such a mission, the emperor considered the consequences--that from the prowess of the one sent, the strength and valor of all his men must be judged, either shame and disgrace for them if he was defeated, or reward and glory if he conquered. He granted that it be done according to the ruling of the senate.

Armis itaque bene et decenter instructum et munitum eum
imperator cum legatis dirigit centum ei insuper cum uno
centurione adjunctis equitibis, ut et honorifice pergeret, et
siquid sibi per tanta terrarum marisve spacia adversi
contigisset, eorum amminiculo evitaret. Nec mora viam ineunt,   5
et ad mare Adriaticum devenientes naves conscendunt. Erant
autem rates cum [26r,col.2] eis xvi quarum alias negociantes,
alias ad loca sancta properantes, ob piratarum seviciam qui per
maris latitudinem vagabantur in eorum comitatu coadunaverant.
Hiis igitur conjunctis, portum deserentes, in altum deferuntur.   10
Quo diebus xxv tumidis jactati fluctibus, dum nec portum petere,
nec rectum possent cursum dirigere; undique procellis
surgentibus, magnisque circumacti anfractibus, ad quandam
insulam gentis barbarice appulsi sunt. Cuius incole tante
feritatis existebant, ut nulli sexui, nulli pacerent etati,   15
quin sontes et insontes ab extranea nacione venientes pari
pena multarent. Ideoque a nullo petebantur sectante commercia,
sed ab omni gente cui tante infamia nequicie innotuerat
vitabantur; manebantque in orbe quasi extra orbem positi, ab
omnium consorcio segregati. Nam et omnium pecudum ac volucrum   20
carne vesci immodiceque dicuntur volumptati subditi, ut nec
patres filios, nec filii a quibus sint geniti prossus agnoscant.
Trium cubitorum statura mensuram non excedit, etasque ad
quinquagesimum annum protenditur. Raro aliquis infra x vita
diffungitur; nec quinquagesimum supervivens annum transgreditur.   25

---

9. coadunaverant MS: coudunaverant, Bruce 15. sexui: added above
the line MS. pacerent MS: parcerent, Bruce 19. orbe: orbem MS
with 'm' partially blotted out. 23. cubitorum repeated and crossed
out MS. 25. diffungitur: diffungdur MS, corrected above the line.

The emperor directed that the knight, along with the delegation, be well equipped and properly provisioned and that a hundred knights with a centurion in command escort them, so that not only would the knight go forth with honor but also whatever hostility might confront him through such an expanse of land or sea, he could thwart it with their help. Without delay they began the journey, and reaching the Adriatic Sea they boarded ships. There were sixteen other vessels along with theirs, some of which were merchantmen, others fast ships bound for the Holy Land which had joined their convoy because of the savage pirates who roamed the wide seas. The ships formed up, left the harbor, and set sail for deep water.

For twenty-five days they were tossed on huge waves, unable either to seek haven or to steer a straight course; beset by mounting gales and driven in great circles, they were brought to shore on an island of a barbarous people. The inhabitants were of such savagery that they would arrange no safe conduct for anyone either for sex or for age, but would inflict punishment on all landing from outside, whether guilty or innocent. For this reason they were approached by no one seeking trade, and branded with a reputation for such cruelty, they were shunned by all; they remained within the world just short of being outside it, cut off from the society of all others. They are said to consume voraciously the meat of all cattle and fowl; and since they are so dominated by passions of the flesh, the fathers do not know their own sons, nor the sons know precisely by whom they were fathered. Their stature ranges to three cubits, and their life expectancy is fifty years. Rarely does anyone die before the tenth year or live beyond fifty.

Cultu cibisque diffusi, laboribus assueti, diviciis affluentes
in propagacione sobolis noscuntur fecundi. Jam vero fama per
omnes paganorum regiones percrebuerat, militem ab imperatore
missum ad initum venire duellum cuius congressum nemo sufferre
valebat. [26v,col.1]   Ideoque   ad   universas   sue   dicionis   5
insulas Egeo Mari quod transfretaturus erat adjacentes, clanculo
mandaverant, ut portus et littora jugi excubacione observarent,
et si forte appulisset, opprimerent, ne ad statutum diem venire
potuisset. Nec non et piratas diversis in locis lata equoris
statuerant obsidere spacia, ut si ab hostia observantibus minime   10
lesi evasissent ab hiis qui per fretum usque discurrebant
inopinate exciperentur. Regnabat autem ea tempestate in illa
insula quidam dictus Milocrates inimicus Romani populi qui
neptem imperatoris quam regi Illirico dederat vi capiens et
abducens; illam insulam potencia occupaverat. Huic quoque sicut   15
et ceteris notificatis insidiis, civitates et oppida que vel
pelago imminebant, seu penes quas aptos applicantibus portus
fore compererat, militibus et custodibus munierat ut et ille
transeuntem infestarent, et hee appellentes subito invaderent.
Littora autem quibus applicuerant per girum erant circumdata   20
nemoribus, minus tamen opima agrestibus animalibus. Unde ob
eorum raritatem et ab incolis extraneisque supervenientibus
arcius seduliusque servabantur, quorum esu, rege excepto ac eius
principibus, nulli fas erat perfrui.

---

6. Egeo Mari MS: in Egeo Mari, Bruce 11. lesi: le lesi MS, Bruce
13. Milocrates: also written in margin in Greek letters. 17. aptos:
aptus MS, Bruce 19. hee=eae

26

Accustomed to hard work, they are known for their cultivation and production of food. They abound in wealth and they have many children.

The news had spread through all pagan lands that a knight whose passage at arms no one could withstand was being sent by the emperor to undertake the duel. For that reason, to all the islands in the Aegean Sea under pagan control near which he would have to pass, secret orders were sent to set a constant watch over ports and shores and, if by chance the knight should come to land, to overpower him so that he would not be able to arrive on the designated day. Not only that, they directed pirates to blockade the open reaches of the sea in different areas so that if the men escaped unharmed by those on guard at the ports, they might be taken by others patrolling the intervening seas.

Reigning at this time on that island was a man named Milocrates, an enemy of the Roman people, who had captured and abducted by force the emperor's niece whom the emperor himself had betrothed to the King of Illyricum.* He had seized military control of the island. Since these stratagems had been made known to him as to the others, he fortified with soldiers and guards the cities and towns that lay near the sea or possessed ports which he had learned were suitable for landing ships, so that his soldiers could attack them as they approached or the guards capture them at once if they landed. However, the shores by which the Romans did come to land were lined with dense forests in every direction, not the best land for animals of the field.

Because of this scarcity, the wild beasts were protected quite carefully and strictly from the local people as well as from outsiders who might land. According to the law, no one was to have the pleasure of eating this game save the king himself or his princes.

5

10

15

20

25

30

27

Hanc igitur ubi prefatus centurio cum sua classe est
nactus insulam, Miles cum tunica armature paucis comitantibus
puppim egressus silvas venatum adiit. Jamque vi prostratis
[26v,col.2] discopulatis canibus vii insequi cervum ceperat, dum
ecce canum latratus tubarumque strepitus, in interiorem silvam   5
positus custos percepit nemoris. Accitisque sociis quorum
tutele secum silva tuenda a rege commissa fuerat; arma jubet
capere. Nam xx milites qui illam tuerentur disponebantur,
quorum absque licencia nulli tutus in ea pacebat ingressus.
Arma jussi capiunt atque venantibus jam preda potitis occurrunt.   10
Querunt cuius licencia regia depopulentur nemora, que nec eciam
ingressu pacifico subire cuiquam licebat. Jubentur arma
deponere, atque pro temeritate patrata judicium subituri regem
adire. E contra Miles cum tunica armature respondit, "Cuius huc
advenimus, eiusque licencia nobis necessaria invadimus. Nec   15
arma nisi in vestris visceribus recondita deponemus."

    Dixerat et valido et contorquens pila lacerto,

    In tumido rigidum congessit guttere ferrum;

    Cuius dextra gravis compescuit ora minantis.

Custos autem nemoris saucius ingemuit; sed tamen ipso dolore   20
magis intumuit; atque e plaga extractum toto conamine missile in
Militem cum tunica armature remisit, quod ab eo errore delatum
robori infixum est. Nec mora hinc et inde concurrunt

1-23. cf. Geof. Hist. 1.12. 9. pacebat MS: patebat, Bruce
17-19. hexameters identified by meter Meyer, Rajna. MS has the
symbol of slashed "v" in margin. 17. et MS: omitted, Bruce
contorquens: torquens MS, Bruce 18. guttere MS: gutture, Bruce

28

So it happened that when the centurion mentioned earlier
and the fleet under his command had made landfall on this
island, the Knight of the Surcoat disembarked with a few
companions to hunt. Six stags were soon slain, and with dogs
set loose he had begun to pursue the seventh when suddenly the 5
keeper of the preserve, stationed in the interior of the forest,
heard the baying of the hounds and the blasts of the horns. The
keeper summoned his companions who were under the king's orders
to guard the forest with him; he commanded them to arm
themselves. Twenty knights had been deployed to protect the 10
forest; without their permission no one was allowed safe entry.
As ordered, these men took up arms and went out to confront the
hunters who were already in possession of the quarry. The
foresters demanded by whose authority they poached on the royal
game preserve into which no one was allowed entrance even with 15
peaceful intent. They ordered the hunters to lay down their
weapons and go before the king to submit to his judgment for the
rash act they had committed.

To this the knight responded, "For these deer we have come
and we took them because of our need, and we will not sheathe 20
our weapons unless we sheathe them in your guts."

He spoke, and brandishing spears with a powerful arm,
He hurled cold steel into the arrogant throat;
With his powerful right arm he stopped the mouth of the
    menacing one. 25

The wounded keeper of the preserve groaned, but he was so
enraged by the intensity of the pain that when he had wrenched
the missile from the wound, with supreme effort he flung it back
at the Knight of the Surcoat, yet because his arm shook, it was
thrown awry and struck a tree. 30

29

ceteri; et nunc cominus consertis dextris sibi invicem vulnera
ingerunt, nunc eminus telorum jactu confligunt. Ex parte quidem
Militis cum tunica armature plures habebantur sed inermes; cum
adversariis omnium munimen armorum adesset. At Miles cum tunica
armature dum suos cedere videret hostibus, stricto gladio   5
[27r,col.1] in eorum ducem irruens, humo prostravit
apprehensoque naso cassidis eum ad socios traxit; ac vita cum
armis destituit. Quibus ipse indutus, propriam hortatus turmam
invasit hostilem, ceterisque fugatis xiii solus peremit.
Fugientes vero per silvarum abdita turba insequitur militum;   10
omnesque quos assequi possunt ad Tartara dirigunt. Cui cedi
unus superstes relinquitur ut tante cladis existat nuncius. Is
inter densa fruticum se oculens delituit; donec manus adversaria
discendens se desisteret persequi. Qua recedente, ocius
surrexit regem adiit, atque ei que gesta fuerant retulit.   15
Morabatur autem tunc temporis rex Milocrates in finitima
civitate quam tribus milibus a mari amenissimo in loco
condiderat. Qui hostium adventu suorumque militum interitu
congnito, missis continuo nunciis tocius provincie principes cum
quanta manu valerent, quantocius convenire imperat. Illi autem   20
ut imperatum erat et loco et tempore cum collecta multitudine
adveniunt. Advenientes autem per vicinos pagos hospitabantur,
quia predicta eos civitas capere non poterat. Rex vero
Milocrates cum eorum principibus quid agendum foret
deliberabat.   25

---

4. munimen MS: muninen, Bruce

30

At once the rest of the men from either side attacked; now grappling in close conflict, hand to hand they slashed at each other, now from a distance they fought by hurling spears. Actually the Knight of the Surcoat had more men, but none of them were wearing armor, while all their adversaries were fully protected. But the Knight of the Surcoat, when he saw his own men giving way before the enemy, drew his sword, and rushing their leader, knocked him to the ground, grabbed the noseguard of his helmet, dragged him to his own men, and stripped him of his life and his armor together. Having equipped himself with this armor, shouting for his men, he attacked the enemy, and though some fled, he alone slew thirteen.

The hunting party followed the fugitives through the forest and sent to Tartarus all they could overtake. Only one man was left as a survivor to be the messenger of so great a defeat. He had hidden himself out of sight within the dense foliage until his adversaries had stopped searching for him and gone away.

When they had left, he rose up quickly, went to the king, and related what had happened. King Milocrates was staying at that time in a nearby city that he had founded in a most delightful setting three miles from the sea. When he learned of the landing of the enemy and the slaying of his knights, he at once dispatched messengers and ordered the princes of all the provinces to come together as quickly as possible with as many men as they could muster. They complied with the command in time and place and came with a vast army. Those arriving were lodged throughout the neighboring countryside because the king's city was not able to hold them. Then King Milocrates deliberated with his princes what they must do.

31

Interea Miles cum tunica armature devictis hostibus ad
naves regreditur, cuius victorie adeptis remuneratus spoliis
omnis congratulatur exercitus. Die autem tercia inceptum
affectabatur iter aggredi; sed flabris obstantibus, in [27r,
col.2] loco coacti sunt remorari. Centurio igitur nimis inde   5
afflictus majores milicie congregat, atque ab eis de patrandis
negociis consilium expetit. Affirmabat enim regem illius insule
eiusque principes ob suorum perniciem jam se contra moveri,
eosque in ulcionem peremptorum se oppressum ire jam conspirasse,
ni discessum cicius maturassent. Se autem sibi aura remittente   10
inde discendere non valere, nec tutum fore illuc dicebat
manendum, dum nec ad multitudinis repulsionem hostium militum
haberetur copia, nec suis expensis tam longo in tempore
necessaria suppeterent. "Oportet," inquid, "igitur quempiam
nostrum vires et consilia investigatum ire adversariorum, ut   15
cognitis que penes eos factitantur, que nobis agenda sunt
utilius provideamus." Dicta ducis placent, atque qui hoc
exerceant negocium duo de omnibus eliguntur, quorum unus Miles
cum tunica armature, alter Odabel dictus centurionis exstabat
consanguineus qui et in dubiis providi et cauti, et in adversis   20
probi et strenui pre ceteris noscebantur. Hii armis septi
jussum iter arripiunt, atque per nemus ad urbem tendunt.

14. inquid MS: inquit, Bruce

Meanwhile, the Knight of the Surcoat, having overcome the
foresters, returned to the ships. The entire contingent,
rewarded with the spoils of victory, congratulated him. Then on
the third day they attempted to get on with the voyage they had
begun, but because the winds continued to be unfavorable they   5
were forced to remain where they were.

The centurion, quite disturbed by the delay, assembled the
leaders of the knights and sought from them counsel about what
could be done toward proceeding with their mission. He assumed,
further, that the king of that island and his princes were now   10
moving against them in retaliation for their resistance, and
that they had by now mobilized to crush them in vengeance for
those deaths--and would do so, unless they could quickly get
under way. He contended that unless the wind abated for them,
they lacked the strength to row the ships from that place, nor   15
would it be safe to remain there while they had too few knights
to fight off the great numbers of the enemy, nor would their
provisions of food and fodder last much longer.

"It is necessary then," the centurion began, "that some of
our men go spy on the manpower and plans of the enemy so that   20
when we know how he usually deploys his forces we may foresee
more practically what must be done."

The words of the leader were well received, and two of the
men were chosen to perform the task. One of them was the Knight
of the Surcoat; the other, named Odabel, was a blood relative of   25
the centurion. They were known in uncertain situations to be
careful and prudent, and in danger to be stronger and more
skillful than the others. Protected with armor, they began the
journey as ordered and made their way through the forest to the
city.   30

In cuius silve aditu aper illis immanis occurrit, colla ad modum
hastilium setis obsitus, aduncis dentibus rictus munitus, ab
cuius ore fulmine evaporante, spumaque per armos fluente;
obliquo in illo impetu ferebatur. Miles cum tunica armature
autem illo viso de sonipede desiliit, ac splendidum dextra   5
vibrans venabulum, antequam se copiam aggrediendi haberet in
illo pedes [27v,col.1] irruit. Cuius fronti inter supercilia
infixum spiculum; cetera percurrens sibi per ilia fecit exitum.
Nec tamen statim corruit, sed cum accepto vulnere, furorem
concepisse videbatur ut tametsi deficiente sanguine vires   10
plurimum defecissent quantumvis dabatur eum cum dente impeteret.
Opposito vero egide dum ictum Miles cum tunica armature
exciperet; evaginato gladio capud in se furentis abscidit, ac
eum in suo cruore volutantem dimisit. Quem equo impositum
ipsius armiger sui ex parte ad centurionem detulit; atque   15
citato cursu rediens, illum ad urbis valvas mediante die
anticipavit. Civitatem autem introgressi, palacium adire
mixtique cum aliis inter regales quasi forent ex ipsis
conversabantur. Innumerosa namque turba eos qui essent non
deprehensi sinebat dum eciam et hoc ad eorum accidisset tutelam 20
quod illius patrie lingue periciam non ignorabant. Urbem itaque
pagosque quoquoversus perlustrantes virtutem numerumque milicie
investigabant, aut que presens aderat, ceu quam fore venturam
audierant. Minime quippe adhuc omnis exercitus convenerat.

1-14. cf.Ovid, Meta. 8.11.   5. desiliit: desilii MS, corrected
in margin. 12. opposito: oposito MS, Bruce   14. equo: eco MS, Bruce
21. periciam: periticam MS, Bruce

At the entrance to the king's forest an enormous boar rushed upon them, its neck covered with bristles like shafts, its gaping jaws armed with curved tusks, thunder roaring from its mouth, and saliva spewing over its forequarters. It charged at an angle to the attack. Seeing it, the Knight of the Surcoat 5 leaped from his horse and, brandishing a flashing hunting spear in his right hand, struck a blow before it had a chance to strike. The spearhead pierced into its foreskull between the brows; forced on through the body, it came out above the flank. Yet not only did the boar not fall immediately, but with the 10 wound received it seemed to gather fury, so that although its strength was diminished greatly by the loss of blood, with all the might it could muster it could still attack him with its tusks. While blocking the slash, the Knight of the Surcoat took the blow on his shield, unsheathed his sword, cut off the head 15 of the beast as it was raging at him, and left it rolling around in its own blood. The beast was lifted onto the armorbearer's horse, and the armorbearer delivered it to the centurion on their behalf.

Returning quickly to the path, the knight was waiting for 20 him at the gates of the city by midday. When they entered the city, they proceeded to the palace and mingled with the king's men as if they belonged with them. Actually the very large number of men made it possible for them to go unnoticed as strangers, while as an additional safeguard, they had a 25 practical knowledge of the language of that country. They scoured the city and also the rural regions in every direction, noting the strength and number of military groups and which specific ones were present, for they had heard which ones were yet to come. By no means had the entire army assembled.

35

Pridie namque rex Milocrates classem Romanorum quosdam exploratum miserat, qui repedantes oppido eum terruerant, se tantam astipulantes armatorum repperisse multitudinem, quantam inermium eius insula nunquam continuisset. Exploratores siquidem a centurione capti fuerant, quos illo ibi mortem 5 minantem, se talia ducturos sacramento spondere coegerat. Insuper et eis quo eos [27v,col.2] sibi fideliores haberet, plurima dona largitus ad propria eos dimisit. Unde rex Milocrates classem invasum ire nisi cum forti manu verebatur. Germanum autem suum Buzafarnan nomine confinia regna regentem 10 per legatos acciverat; ut sibi in tanta necessitate quanta et quam cicius posset conferret presidia. Cuius eo adventum expectante, belli protelabantur negocia. Eo autem die quo Miles cum tunica armature urbem advenerat, rex forte Milocrates optimatum conventum coegerat, ab eis sciscitans quid in rebus 15 instantibus factu opus foret. In quo ab omnibus statutum est ut eius fratre rege Buzafarnan adventante, exercitus duabus distingueretur in partibus, e quibus una navali, alia terrestri adversarios aggrederetur prelio, ut nullus fuge locus pateret. Miles vero cum tunica armature inter alios incognitus residens, 20 singula que dicebantur intenta aure percepta memori mente notabat.

---

5. a: autem corrected to a in MS; illo MS: illi, Bruce   6: minantem MS: menans, Bruce   ducturos MS: dicturos, Bruce

Actually, on the day before King Milocrates had sent some men to spy out the fleet of the Romans, and when they returned to the city, they had terrified him by reporting so great a multitude of armored men that his island did not even contain as many without armor. Further, the spies had been captured by the centurion, and under threat of immediate death, he had compelled them to swear under oath that they would falsify the count. In order that he might make them even more loyal to himself, in addition to the threats he also sent them away with a great many lavish gifts for their own keeping. As a result, King Milocrates feared that the fleet had invaded with no less than an overwhelming force. Through messengers he summoned his own brother, Buzafarnan by name, who reigned over a nearby kingdom, so that he might bring him help in his great need, just as much and as fast as he could. While he waited for his brother's arrival, the action of the attack was postponed. On the day that the Knight of the Surcoat came to the city, King Milocrates had called the assembly of the nobility, discussing with them what steps to take in this emergency. The consensus was that when his brother Buzafarnan arrived the army should be divided into two parts, one for ship and the other for land, so that when they engaged the enemy in battle no route would be open for escape. The Knight of the Surcoat, who remained unrecognized among them and listened intently, noted what each man said and committed the plan to memory.

Jamque Phebus occiderat, et rex Milocrates ad prandium
festinabat. In cuius comitatu se agens, Miles cum tunica
armature sociis se aforis opperientibus, regiam ingreditur,
ceterisque discumbentibus, cubiculum quo neptis imperatoris,
scilicet regina quam rex Milocrates ut pretaxavimus legitimo   5
viro abstulerat, cum suis dumtaxat residebat puellis, nullo
subit sciente. Tardior quippe ora visus hebetaverat, sed
necquid tale posse contingere aliquis autumabat. Cepit autem
quid   ageret apud se de[28r,col.1]liberare,   et quicquid
sinistri   sibi   obvenire valerat,   sedulo mentis oculo   10
providere. Si enim ut proposuerat in thalamo delitescens,
regi sopito   necem inferret,   verberabatur ne et ipse
deprehensus similem penam lueret. Si autem nulla probitate
patrata repedasset profecto   pro inerte timidoque haberetur.
Dum talia secum volveret,   quidam miles Nabaor nunccupatus,   15
unus scilicet ex illis quos nuper rex classem centurionis
exploratum miserat, missus a rege ad reginam advenit; intuebatur
eum Miles cum tunica armature, nec ab illo advertebatur. Mos
quippe est quod in umbra consitituti, luci presentes clare
aspiciant; ipsique ab illis incircumspecti maneant. Hunc sibi   20
Miles cum tunica armature dum cum aliis exploratoribus a
centurione captus teneretur, firma junxerat amicicia;
anulumque ei cum purpurea clamide, ob sui tradiderat memoriam.

---

8. autumabat: attumabat MS, Bruce   12. verberabatur MS: verebatur
Bruce 14. inerte: inte corrected in MS.   15. MS has two spellings,
Nabaor and Nabor. 20. sibi MS: igitur, Bruce

38

Already Phoebus the sun had set, and King Milocrates
hurried to his evening meal. The Knight of the Surcoat, placing
himself in his company, entered the royal palace while his
companions waited outside for his return. When the rest of the
king's men had reclined to eat, the knight slipped out unnoticed   5
toward the bedchamber where the niece of the emperor—that is,
the queen, whom King Milocrates, as we have said, had stolen
from her lawful husband—resided alone with her maidens. The
rather late hour had dimmed visibility; still it was said that
chamber was unapproachable. He began to deliberate what in his   10
judgment must be done and to plan carefully, picturing in his
mind how he would have strength to meet whatever traps he might
encounter. If, for instance, he was to hide in the bedchamber
and kill the king while he was asleep, as he had originally
planned, he was tormented knowing that he himself, caught in the   15
act of murder, would suffer the same punishment. On the other
hand, if he returned to the ship with no deed accomplished, he
would be rightfully considered a slacker and a coward. While he
turned such things over in his mind, a certain knight named
Nabaor—one, in fact, of those whom the king not long before had   20
sent to spy on the fleet of the centurion—came along, having
been sent by the king to the queen. The Knight of the Surcoat
could see him clearly, but he himself remained unnoticed by the
man. (Those standing in the shadows see clearly those in the
light while they themselves remain unseen by others.) While   25
this man was held captive by the centurion with the other spies,
the Knight of the Surcoat had struck up a strong friendship with
him; for remembrance he had shared with him a ring and a crimson
chlamys.*

39

Eo igitur viso, ex amicicia audaciam sumit eumque ad se clanculo
acciens, amplectitur causam adventus insinuat, atque quedam
quibus eius ergasse experiretur prelocutus favorem; ubi eum sibi
remota fraude animum advertit favere, ad ea que mente perceperat
perpetranda sibi subsidio fore supplicatur. Nabaor autem   5
admodum ex eius presencia admiratur, et cur venerit cognito,
eius remunerandi munificenciam locum se invenisse gaudebat.
Secriori itaque ei inducto thalamo, "O mi," inquit, "karissime,
tuo posse majus est quod affectas, nec tuis solis viribus
appetendum. Triginta namque forcium [28r,col.2] regis accubitus   10
pervigiles ambiunt, uti nec eciam eius familiaribus usque dum
dies lucescat ad eum fiat accessus. Preterea plerisque
temporibus industria pocius quam viribus scias utendum; quia
eciam ex parte virium industria multociens quod cupitur prospere
efficitur, sine qua ad successum negocii nunquam viribus   15
venitur. Hac autem comite propositum aggredere, me tamen te quo
ordine agatur docente. Regina tui nimio detinetur amore, teque
vel alloqui seu per internuncios tua cognicione ardentissime
cupit potiri. A me enim ab exploratoris redeunte officio, cuius
forme statureque sis sepius est percunctata, quem utrisque   20
incomparabilem esse respondens, eius animum in tui accendi
amorem ut pocius de tui quam de regis occupetur salute.

4. animum MS: animo, Bruce 6. cur: cum MS, Bruce 11. eius: added
above line MS. 19. cuius MS: cuuis Bruce

Recognizing him then and gambling on this friendship, the Knight of the Surcoat summoned him secretly, embraced him, hinted at the reason for his coming, and by some preliminary remarks tested his feelings toward him in these matters. When he perceived that he would give protection to him, forsaking all pretense, he asked the man to help him accomplish what he had in mind. Nabaor, for his part, wondered greatly about his presence and when he learned why he had come was delighted to have found the chance to return his generosity.

So after leading him to a private chamber, he began thus, "My beloved friend, what you desire is greater than what you can accomplish, and it ought not be undertaken by your strength alone. For thirty very strong men, always on watch, surround the couch of the king; thus no one is allowed access to him until daylight, not even his servants. Besides, you know that on the whole you must employ more care than strength, because what is longed for is often accomplished successfully by careful planning in support of strength. Strength without cunning never gets the job done. Follow this advice as you approach your venture, but with me to guide you in what order it is to be carried out. The queen is greatly attracted to you and she desires most ardently to make your acquaintance either by addressing you in person or through intermediaries. She has often inquired of me after I returned from my duty as a spy what form and stature you have, and I, replying that you are incomparable in both, kindled her heart with love for you, so that she is more concerned with your welfare than with the king's.

Quamquam nimirum ut huius regina patrie maximo a rege Milocrate
honoris et glorie sullimetur fastigio, tamen quia se a maritali
thoro captam jure predonis menti non excidit, semper se
captivitatis remordet obprobrium, malletque alias cum paupere
libera quam hinc omni rerum pompa suffulta, degere captiva.   5
Audiens autem te ob ingenitam incomparabilemque probitatem ab
imperatore ad pactum destinatum, conflictum huc appulisse, toto
conamine nititur, omni studio molitur ut tuum modo adipisci
possit alloquium. Sperat namque si tuam attingat noticiam, se
tua virtute et fortitudine a captivitatis jugo liberandam, et   10
suo marito cui ab im[28v,col.1]peratore dotata noscitur
restituendam. Sciasque procul dubio omni industria et ingenio
illam operam adhibituram, omni ab illa sagacitate curandum ut
tibi vires et valorem augeat et adversum regem Milocraten
prevalere efficiat. Verumptamen quia mens muliebris levitatis   15
nota arguitur et ad quoslibet motus inconstancie cicius aura
flectitur, prius callide temptandum est, quorsum eius vergat
affectus. Que si te adesse comperisset, nec regis timor, nec
fame pudor eam arceret, quin tecum verba consereret. Pergam
igitur ad eam regis ei mandata laturus, atque inter cetera de te 20
sollerte mencionem faciens, cui parti eius innitatur investigabo
voluntas. Tu vero hic interim rei latenter eventum exspecta."

10. liberandam MS: iiberandam, Bruce 14. Milocraten MS, Greek
accusative form. 22. exspecta MS: expecta, Bruce

42

Though doubtless the queen of this country has been raised to the highest degree of honor and glory by King Milocrates, still because she has not forgotten she was abducted from the marriage bed by right of plunder, the shame of captivity continuously torments her, and she would even now prefer to be free with a poor man than to continue supported here with all ostentation of property as a captive. Hearing that you have landed here, on mission to the sworn duel for the emperor because of your inborn and incomparable prowess, she yearns desperately and avidly desires that it be possible simply to have a chance to speak to you. For she hopes if she gains your attention that she can be freed from the yoke of captivity and restored to her own husband for whom the marriage portion was approved by the emperor. You know without doubt that this venture will require employing every effort and cunning; it will require from her commitment with all sagacity, so that your strength and courage may be effective and allow you to prevail against King Milocrates. Yet because a woman's mind is always changing with random moods more quickly than the wind, one must first discreetly test in which direction her disposition is inclined. If this woman has learned you are here, neither fear of the king nor shame of gossip will keep her from coming to you; she will still speak with you. I shall go to her, then––being sent to carry her the king's messages––and among others things I mention, I'll speak of you artfully and learn where her will is inclined. You, meanwhile, stay hidden here until I know the outcome."

Reginam itaque Nabaor adiit, inter quos dum varia miscerentur colloquia, de Milite cum tunica armature tandem sermo habitus est. Quem dum Nabaor de miris ab eo patratis operibus multa laude efferret, "O me felicem," inquit regina, "si apud tam probum virum mee valerem miserie querelam   5
deponere, profecto si non ob aliud, saltim ob imperatoris graciam, cuius neptis ego sum et cuius miles ipse est, me ab huius erriperet tirannide. Vellem igitur si quempiam fidelem invenirem ad eum nuncium mittere, si quomodo nos visendi et colloquendi nobis detur facultas." Erat autem Nabaor cum quo   10
illa loquebatur unus ex illis quos una secum rex Milocrates servitutis vinculo mancipaverat. Ideoque [28v,col.2] illi ut suorum secretorum conscio sue mentis tucius committebat archana. Cui ille respondit, "Nil tuis, O Regina, impedimento fore votis rearis, si tibi dumtaxat huiusmodi inest affectus, nec nuncii   15
opus erit tantum fraus desit dictis tantummodo concordet voluntas, et quem adeo affectas presto pro voto aderit." Illa autem ad hec jurante, id se velle optabilius fieri quam audere profiteri, Nabaor Militem cum tunica armature ante eam duxit; et rem ei pro qua venerat pandit. Porro ut superius ostensum est,   20
ille statura virilis decorus exstabat aspectu; quo se aspecciencium oculos in se pre decoris admiracione converteret.

---

1. Reginam: Regina MS, Bruce   15. nuncii: nunci MS, Bruce

Nabaor accordingly approached the queen. Between them, as various topics of conversation were discussed, there was talk concerning the Knight of the Surcoat.

As Nabaor narrated his marvelous deeds with much praise, the queen replied, "How happy I'd be if I could address to so 5 worthy a man my heartfelt distress! Certainly if for no other reason than the favor of the emperor whose niece I am and whose knight he is, he would rescue me from this man's tyranny. I desire, therefore, to find someone trustworthy to send as a messenger to him, so that in one way or another he may be given 10 the opportunity of seeing and talking with us."

Nabaor, to whom she was talking, was also one of those whom Milocrates had captured with her and forced into chains of servitude. Thus to that man as fellow-conspirator of her secrets she safely committed the private confidences of her 15 heart.

He replied to her, "My Queen, you may reckon nothing as an impediment to your wishes, if you are thus disposed, nor will there be need of a messenger. Only let yourself be free from deceit, only let your wishes agree with your words, and he whom 20 you desire so much will be present as you command."

And when she had sworn in reply that she wanted this to be done more eagerly than she had dared confess, Nabaor led the Knight of the Surcoat into her presence, and he laid open to her the purpose for which he had come. Moreover, as was earlier 25 understood, he stood forth handsome to her sight with a manly build which drew glances in his direction from people amazed at his beauty.

Quem venientem regina salutans, assidere fecit, diuque
diligenter eum contemplata, tandem lacrimis erumpentibus, imo ex
pectore suspiria protulit, et quibus gravaretur erumpnis aperuit
eum sibi adiciens tantorum malorum posse conferre, si vellet
remedium; et ille, "Si meum velle posse comitaretur, nempe   5
nullius in agendo more fieret dilacio. Sed patet regem numero
et virtute nobis prestare milicie, et iccirco incertum est quis
nos belli maneat exitus. Unde si quid calles quod tuis votis
succedere, quod optatum negocium prospero possit fine terminare
innotesce, nec me pigrum desidemve in exequendo advertes." Ad   10
que dum regina reticens paululum que diceret cogitaret, Nabaor
ait, "Minime te latet, O Regina, regem coadunare exercitum,
contra hos [29r,col.1] dimicaturum. Sub cuius frequencia
maximam rebus agendis video adesse oportunitatem. Poteris enim
si eius tanta cura teneris, et hunc cum sociis ab instanti   15
subtrahere periculo, et tuum affectum ad optatum effectum
perducere. Regis quippe animus belli occupatus negociis, minus
de ceteris exstabit solicitus. Manda igitur centurioni per hunc
xl armis instructos huc die postera clanculo per silvarum oppaca
delegare, ut sequente die rege contra se ineunte certamen, te   20
eam tradente illi civitatem occupent que igne incensa regi suis-
que horrendum spectaculum; illis autem victorie causam prebeat."

---

11. paululum: palulum MS, Bruce 16. ad optatum MS: adoptatum Bruce

The queen, greeting him as he entered, bade him sit down, and having contemplated him intensely for some time, finally burst into tears, brought forth a deep sigh from her breast and laid open the distress by which she was burdened, adding that he could bestow on her, if he were willing, the remedy of such   5
great evils.

He replied, "If my desire could be joined by equal ability, without doubt there would be no delay in obeying your will. But it is plain that the king exceeds us in the number and strength of his soldiers, and it is uncertain for that reason what   10
conclusion to the war awaits us. If you know anything which could help us bring this undertaking to a successful end, tell me and you will not find me either slack or slow in carrying it out."

While the queen, pausing for a moment, considered what she   15
would say to this, Nabaor spoke. "It is by no means hidden from you, my queen, that the king is summoning the army against these men for what will be a pitched battle. In the great mass of this army I see the best opportunity for taking action. If, therefore, you are burdened with such concern, you have the   20
means both to remove him and his comrades from the impending disaster and also to accomplish what you have longed for so intensely. The king's attention, fixed on the strategies of war, will be less concerned with other matters. Command, then, through the knight, that the centurion delegate forty armed men   25
and send them here tomorrow through the depth of the forest in secret, so that the day after, when the king advances against him in battle, they will occupy the city, which you will betray to them, and when they have set it on fire, the horrible spectacle for the king and his men will provide the means of   30
victory."

Illa vero que dicta sunt eum multis precibus peragere rogitat. Ensem regis preterea ac eius arma ei contulit aurea, de quibus fatatum erat quod ab eo devictus rex regali spoliaretur apice, qui preter ipsum ea primitus induisset. Auri quoque et argenti, magnique gemmarum precii copiosa accumulavit munera; insuper et   5
amicicie conjunxit federa. Quibus gestis, ad socios Miles cum tunica armature festinanter revertitur; quos ab urbe educens diluculo ad centurionem pervenit. Cum dona sibi collata ostendens que gesserat, viderat, audierat intimavit.

Centurio igitur ultra quam credi potest pro spe exhilaratus   10 victorie, jussit milites qui ad reginam destinarentur eligi. Electis vero Odabel suum prefecit consanguineum, eumque ut caute et provide sibi commissos duceret hortatus, dimisit, per[29r,col.2]gentes itaque ad vineam que regie confinis erat, die secunda jam vesperascente pervenere in qua jussu regine a   15 Nabaor intromissis nocte tota latuere.

Mane autem illucescente, rex Milocrates contra centurionem conflicturus cum exercitu civitatem egreditur, cuius ante majorem partem suo fratre duce, hostes autem tergo invasuram classe permiserat, ut utrimque bello circumdati, cicius sibi cederent.   20

---

16. intromissis MS: intromissi Bruce

48

She entreated him with many prayers to carry out the proposed plan. She then bestowed on the Knight of the Surcoat the king's sword and his gilded armor on which lay the curse that the king, having been overcome, would be stripped of the royal crown by the one who first wore it save for the king himself. In addition she gave him abundant gifts of gold, silver and gems of great value and, above all, sealed the pact with friendship. With these matters settled, the Knight of the Surcoat quickly rejoined his comrades and, leading them from the city, came upon the centurion at first light of dawn. Displaying the gifts he had been given, he also reported what he had done, what he had seen, and what he had heard.

The centurion, exhilarated by hope of victory beyond all expectation, assigned selected knights to go to the queen. When they were chosen, he made his kinsman Odabel the ranking officer, and having urged him to lead those under him with care and foresight, he sent them off toward the vineyard close to the palace as soon as it was dusk, to wait there hidden all night. On the following day Nabaor would admit them by order of the queen.

The next day was dawning when Milocrates marched out of the city with his army to meet the centurion in battle. The larger part of his army he had committed under his brother's leadership to attack the enemy from the rear by ship, so that, having been surrounded on both sides by the fighting, they would surrender more quickly.

49

At centurio percognito eorum consilio, naves in continente circum castra locaverat, ut eciam si opus esset ad se refugientibus forent munimini. Producit et ipse e castris miliciam, que parum ab ponto tuto in loco constituerat. Militesque turmas in v partitur, quarum medie ipsemet preficitur. Gradiebaturque distincte ex regis adverso, quem xv milia armatorum stipabant acies. Sed quamvis numero roboreque precelleret bellatorum, spe tamen minime pociebatur victorie; armis scilicet ablatis in quibus sui regnique constare tutelam noverat. Que dum iturus ad prelia requireret et nequaquam invenisset, omnis boni successus sibi spes menti excidit, nec ea Militem cum tunica armature habere comperiit, donec ipsum illis indutum in campo pungnaturus aspexit. Ad quorum visum nimis perteritus infremuit, quia hoc quod postea evenit sibi nimis vere ratus expavescebat. Non tamen ab incepto valebat desistere quia vel laudabiliter occumbere, vel fortiter vincere; sue videbat glorie expedire.

Clangor igitur utrimque tubarum insonuit, quo et animis audacia et [29v,col.1] hostes aggrediendi signum solet contribui. Manipularesque jam concurrere ceperant, dum ecce fumus de civitate in sullime evaporans, quid in ea ageretur sui declarabat indicio. Ubi namque rex ad pungnam properans ab illa egressus est, confestim hii qui in insidiis morabantur surgentes, illam sue dicioni mancipaverant ac eius suburbana igne inmisso accenderant.

5

10

15

20

25

---

4. tuto: tuo MS, Bruce.

But the centurion, knowing their plan in advance, had re-
located the ships side by side around the camp, so that later if
it became necessary, they would form a rampart for those
retreating to them. From the camp set up in a secure place a
short distance from the sea, the centurion himself led forth the   5
band of knights. He divided the knights and their units into
five squadrons. He himself was the commanding officer of the
center. They were openly moving forward face to face with the
king, who was surrounded in the front line by a thousand armored
men. But however superior in number and strength of warriors   10
the king might be, he held little hope of victory: the armor
upon which he thought rested the protection of himself and his
kingdom had been stolen. When he looked for it as he was
preparing to go into battle and could not find it anywhere, all
hope of success for his plan left him, even though he did not   15
know for certain that the Knight of the Surcoat had it until
finally he saw the man himself clad in it on the field as he was
about to begin the battle. On seeing this he shrieked in great
terror. Supposing only too truly that what later did happen
would happen to him, he was panic-stricken. Still, he was   20
unable to stop what he had begun, and he realized that to
advance his own personal glory he must either conquer
courageously or die bravely.

The blare of trumpets sounded then from both sides, a call   25
which traditionally sounds to inspire a fighting spirit and
signal the attack on the enemy. The foot soldiers had already
begun to make contact when the smoke rising from the city
indicated plainly what was happening there. For as planned,
once the king had led his troops from the city in haste to   30
battle, immediately those waiting in hiding had risen up and
seized control, and they had set aflame the structures below the
walls by throwing fire.

51

Flamma autem altiora petente, remocius positis jam civibus urbis
patebat exitum, ut eciam austro acte per pugnancium ora
volitarent faville. Cor itaque regis pro imminenti expavit
discidio, atque certamine inchoato postposito, succursum ire
urbi festinabat.   5

Agmina turbari telisque manus vacuari;
　　Conspiceresque vage et consuluisse fuge.
Mille vias ineunt, non est tamen una duobus;
　　Sic hostes fugiunt ceu canis ora pecus.   10
Instat et insequitur contraria pars fugientes,
　　Et quos assequitur clade dat esse pares.
Cautibus obruitur pars, pars punita recumbit;
　　Que neutrum patitur vincula dira luit.

                                                                    15

　Miles autem cum tunica armature dissipari, fugarique subito
hostium cuneos conspiciens, conglobato milite insequitur,
maximaque in eis strage crassatur. Quippe quos non solum flamina urbis conflagrans edificia terruerat, verum eciam ipsa quam
inierant fuga eos plurimum mente manuque dissolutos reddiderat.   20
Dispersi itaque per convexa moncium, per devia silvarum, ceu
grex lu[29v,col.2]porum impetitus rabie, ad menia tendebant,
sineque intermissione ab insectancium punibantur gladiis.

2. exitum MS: exitium, Bruce 7-14. Elegiac couplets marked by
slashed V in margin MS. 18. crassatur MS: grassatur, Bruce;
flamina MS: flamma, Bruce

As the flames reached skyward, the catastrophe of the city
was revealed to the citizens already stationed at some distance;
so also ashes carried by the south wind flew into the faces of
the men fighting. The heart of the king was so aghast at the
impending disaster that, disregarding the battle already   5
engaged, he turned quickly to the aid of the city.

You could see the lines in confusion, hands without
    spears,
Men urging dispersal and flight.   10
They go a thousand ways, no two together;
Thus flees the enemy like cattle from a barking dog.
The avengers press on, charge the enemy in flight,
Settle accounts by slaughter of those overtaken.
Rocks bury some, some lie vanquished;   15
He who suffers neither endures the harsh chains.

The Knight of the Surcoat seeing the formations of the
enemy dissolving and suddenly turned to flight, regrouped his
own men and pursued and inflicted mass destruction. Not only   20
had the blast of flame that was consuming the buildings of the
city terrified them, but the very flight they attempted made
them for the most part mentally and physically helpless.
Scattered throughout the declivities of the mountains, through
the unfrequented places of the forests, as a flock attacked by 25
the fury of wolves, they headed toward the city walls, and they
received ceaseless vengeance from the swords of their pursuers.

53

Milites quoque qui exteriorem urbis partem inflammaverant, fugientibus occurrentes, eos a meniis arcebant, et ad campum retorquentes; in eorum quos fugiebant manus compellebant incidere. Fiebat utrimque horrenda cedes ipsaque sui impediebantur numerositate, ut nec ad fugam, nec ad sui   5 defensionem habiles haberentur. Movebantur et absque vindice, ut vulgus inerme, nullusque petenti dextram dare dignatus est.

Tandem autem rex Milocrates ubi se ab hostibus undique circumveniri conspexit sibi fore duxit infame, si nullo claro perpetrato facinore occumberet. Dispersos itaque adunit in   10 cuneum, sibique insistentes viriliter invadens; primo congressu adversariorum refrenat impetum ac sibi compellit cedere. Dextraque quam plures propria puniens ceteros ad fugam vertebat; donec Miles cum tunica armature suos ab illo commilitones male tractari advertens, ei admisso equo   15 obviam fertur. Venientem rex Milocrates audacter excipit; invicemque congressi uterque ab altero equo prosternitur. Ac Miles cum tunica armature cicius erectus, jam surgere conantem, stricto mucrone in regem irruit; letalique affecisset vulnere, ni ictus ab objecto cassaretur clipeo. Quem licet sit   20 nulla secuta lesio magna tamen hebetacio provenit cerebro, ut iterum relapsus unius hore spacio, sopito jaceret similis.

---

1. exteriorem: exeriorem MS, Bruce   10. perpetrato: ppetrato MS, Bruce
15. ei: added margin MS.   21. magna: magma MS, Bruce

The knights who had set fire to the outskirts of the city, meeting the fugitives, kept them away from the walls, and driving them back into the field of battle, forced them to fall into the hands of those from whom they fled. On either hand was the horrible slaughter, and they were impeded by the very numbers of their own men so that they had recourse neither to flight nor to skillful defense. They were shaken and without a protector, like an unarmed rabble, and no one thought it right to give help to him who sought it.

Finally King Milocrates, realizing he was surrounded on all sides by the enemy, reckoned infamy upon himself if he died without some worthy action. He gathered scattered men into a unit and, advancing bravely against his challengers, restrained the force of the enemy in their first encounter and even compelled them to give way before him. With his own right hand he attacked as many as possible and turned the rest to flight, until at length the Knight of the Surcoat, seeing his comrades hard pressed by that man, gave rein to his horse and bore down upon the king. King Milocrates daringly met the charge of the challenger, and as they exchanged blows, each in turn unhorsed the other. But the Knight of the Surcoat, rising more quickly, drew his sword and rushed the king the moment he was struggling to get up. He would have inflicted a fatal wound had not the king blocked the blow with his shield. No great injury resulted, but it so stunned the king's brain that he collapsed and lay for about an hour as if asleep.

55

[30r,col.1] Quem secundo mucrone volenti impetere probus juvenis regis ei nepos occurrit, ac ore et manu minitans, a levo eques Militem cun tunica armature invadit. Cuius incursus Miles cum tunica armature pedes a se scuto protectus reppulit, atque sibi fortuna oblatum, amento intorquens jaculum; non umbo, non ferrea   5 lorica obstitit, quin sub stomacho exceptum, suis majora minitantem viribus cum selle carpella confoderet.

Illo denique prostrato regem repetit, sed majori quam existimaverat ab illo audacia exceptus est. Respiranti namque pudor et ira vires ministraverant pristine dignitatis et probi-   10 tatis eius ante mentis oculos reducentes memoriam; eumque ut se de inimicis ultum iret instimulaverant, se minime ut quempiam plebeium censentes penas solvendum presertim dum sibi non ulla de sui erepcione spes suppeteret, operam dare, ne suis de se leta hostibus proveniret victoria. Advenientem igitur Militem   15 cum tunica armature ipse prior impetit gladio; eiusque qua galea inmunita erat fronti vulnus inflixit nique nasus qui a casside deorsum prominet fuisset presidio una mortem intulisset cum vulnere. Miles cum tunica armature autem sauciatus, mente effrenatur timensque ne profluente visus hebetaretur sanguine; sue ab   20 illo penas exacturus injurie regem aggreditur, ac ensem obliquo cervici ictu inferens, capud cum dextro ei prescidit brachio.

14. operam MS: quam operam, Bruce   22. capud MS: caput, Bruce
15-21. cf. Geof. Historia 9.12.

56

At that moment, the nephew of the king, a skillful young
knight, bore down upon the Knight of the Surcoat as he was
about to dispatch the king with a second thrust of his sword,
and with threats and blows the horseman attacked the Knight of
the Surcoat from the left. The knight on foot repelled the   5
attack with his own shield and, grasping a javelin that had by
luck fallen near him, flung it back by the thong. It was not
stopped by either shield boss or iron lorica, but passing
through the horseman's saddlebow, it pierced deeply under the
belly of one who had made threats beyond his power.   10

Once he had eliminated that attacker, he again sought out
the king, but he was received with a boldness of greater
intensity than he expected. For shame and wrath had brought
back to the king's memory his former dignity and prowess and
given him strength as he regained his breath. He was inspired   15
to avenge himself on the enemy, reckoning that he should not be
punished like some commoner, especially since there was no hope
of rescue. He was determined to expend every effort to prevent
the joy of victory from falling to his enemies. First, then, he
attacked the approaching Knight of the Surcoat, slashed a   20
swordcut across his forehead where it was unprotected by the
helmet, and had not the nosepiece projecting from the helm
blunted it, would have brought death from the gash. The Knight
of the Surcoat, wounded, became frantic with fear that his sight
would be dimmed by the flowing blood, and striving to exact   25
revenge for the injury, he rushed the king and, swinging his
sword with a sidelong blow to the nape of the neck, severed the
head along with the right arm.

57

Quo occumbente, hii qui cum eo [30r,col.2] restiterant, fuga
labuntur, in qua sue sola spes constabat salutis. At centurio,
multitudini parcere volens, tuba ne fugientes persequerentur
militibus significari imperat, sciens duce subacto qui suberant
sine prelio sibi cessuros. Exin hostium collectis spoliis cum   5
triumphali pompa urbem ingrediuntur fornixque eis erigitur.
Quibus regina neptis imperatoris occurrens, eos in regiam ducit
atque bello plurimum fatigatos omni refovet diligencia. Occisis
sepulturam, sauciis curam mandat adhiberi medele; omnibusque se
munificentissimam exhibuit, ac debitis omnes premiis   10
remuneravit.

   Centurio autem apud hanc insulam xv perhendinans diebus,
patriam exercitui diripiendam permisit; principes et magistratus
quod cum hoste Romani populi consensissent serratis carpentis
transegit; populum gravi condicione vectigalium multavit. Parte-   15
que milicie ibi ob tutandam insulam relicta, reginaque nepte
imperatoris cum viris electis ad virum legitimum regem Illirie a
quo vi rapta fuerat remissa, cc^{tis} secum illius provincie assumptis militibus, classem cum sociis refectam ascendit, legacionem quam inceperat perfecturus. Cumque jam per undas equoreas   20
iter confecisset diurnum, eccus regis Milocratis germanus, cuius
regnum obtinuerat, cum classe non minima occurrit. Missus
quippe a rege [30v,col.1] Milocrate, ut prefatum est, antequam
bellum ageretur oppressum classem centurionis fuerat ut utrimque
circumdatus et terra et mari sibi obstrueretur refugium.   25

1. qui: added margin MS. 22. regnum: regum MS, Bruce 23. Milocrate:
first syllable doubled from recto to verso. 24. oppressum: oppresum
MS, Bruce 24. ut: doubled and corrected MS.

When he fell, those who were with him took flight, their only hope of safety. The centurion, wishing to spare the multitude, signalled the knights by trumpet not to pursue the fugitives, knowing that with their leader dead, those under him would surrender without a fight. After collecting the spoils of 5 the enemy, they entered the city with triumphant pomp, and an arch was built in their honor. The queen, niece of the emperor, met them, led them into the palace, and with every attention refreshed those most exhausted by the fighting. She directed that the dead be buried and the wounded cared for with healing 10 remedies, and she showed herself most bountiful to all and rewarded each man according to the prize deserved.

The centurion, staying on at the island for fifteen days, allowed the country to be plundered by the army. Prominent men and administrators, because they had collaborated with the enemy 15 of the Roman people, he had executed and dismembered. He punished the common people by a harsh levy of reparations. Leaving some of the knights there to protect the island and choosing others to accompany the queen, he returned the niece of the emperor to her rightful husband, the King of Illyricum, from 20 whom she had been forcibly seized.

With two hundred additional knights enlisted from that province, he boarded the refurbished fleet with his companions in order to complete the mission that they had undertaken. When he had already completed a day's journey through the waves of the 25 sea, the very brother of King Milocrates, whose kingdom he had conquered, appeared with no small fleet. For, as stated earlier, he had been sent by King Milocrates before the battle to surprise the fleet of the centurion so that, surrounded on all sides, flight for him would be cut off whether by land or sea. 30

59

Sed ad stolum ad stacionem videlicet navium centurionis veniens, nec naves nec eius repererat exercitum. Parumper quippe remocius ab equore castra munierat, ea extrinsecus quoquoversus prora ad sui statuentes munimen. Existimans autem rex Egesarius (sic etenim dicebatur frater regis Milocratis) eos fugisse verso   5 remige in alto defertur equore quo tumidis triduo jactactus fluctibus; dum hostia repetere disponeret, undique procellis surgentibus ad longius remotas provincias itinere dierum v appulsus est. Set jam se aura levius redibat agente; ac medio in pelago centurionis classi habetur obvius.   10

Fortuitu autem ipse centurio in turre quam loco propugnaculi in puppe erexerat, Milite cum tunica armature assidente, residebat, pelagi late visu ambiens spacia. Et primitus quidem simulacra contemplatus est que ad galli aut ad alicuius rei speciem composita malis imponuntur ad   15 experiendum, videlicet quo flabro agatur carina. Cuicumque namque parti mundi climatum flatus vergitur, semper ei adversa fronte obsunt. Hec igitur malis invexa, dum nunc ad altiora, nunc ad inferiora, aura agente pellerentur vexilla. Ceyces ratus, gubernatorem navis advocat, atque, "Heus,"   20 inquit, "ut opinor nobis tempestas [30v,col,2] valida imminet. En namque ut ille volucres pennis applaudentes orbiculatim per inania, cursus dirigunt quasi futurorum prescie sua prelibant gaudia; nostra earum ingluviei predam fore cadavera.

---

2. Parumper: Parum MS 12. propugnaculi: pro pugnaculi MS, Bruce
16. flabro: fabro corrected MS. 22. volucres pennis MS: a correction
indicated in upper margin MS, but most of correction trimmed away.

Although he had reached the fleet, or rather the landing area of
the centurion's ships, he found neither the ships nor the men.
The centurion had hurriedly fortified the camp at some distance
in from the sea and set up the ships as a rampart for his
people, prows pointing outward on all sides. King Egesarius (so   5
the brother of King Milocrates was called) assumed they had
already escaped. Turning his ships about, he sailed back into
deep water, where he was storm-tossed for three days. When he
wanted to come about to seek port again, the winds blowing from
every direction drove him farther off toward distant lands for a   10
five-day voyage. Now with a lighter wind behind him, he had
returned, and he was confronted by the fleet of the centurion in
the midst of the sea.

    By chance, however, the centurion himself was seated in   15
the tower-like structure which he had erected in the stern as a
defense, and with the Knight of the Surcoat sitting near him, he
was scanning the horizons of the sea from this vantage point.
At first he had given attention to figures contrived in the   20
likeness of a cock or some such thing placed on the masts,
doubtless to test by which wind the keel was being propelled.*
For toward whatever corner of the earth the wind of the region
is inclined, these always face into it. The banners, devices
carried on the masts of the approaching fleet, were tossed   25
higher and then lower by the action of the wind.

    The centurion, thinking he saw birds--kingfishers--on the
horizon, shouted to the ship's captain, "Ahoy," and said, "I
think a mighty storm is upon us. For as these birds direct
their course, beating their wings and wheeling through the empty   30
air, so they taste their joys almost with knowledge of the
future, with our corpses about to be food for their crops.

Ferunt quippe imminente procella aves huiusmodi tum gregatim,
tum separatim circa remigantes, crebros girando exercere
volatus, earumque gestus cladem portendere futuram." Miles
autem cum tunica armature tunc ei assistens, et rem ut erat
intelligens, "Tua te," ait, "Domine, fallit opinio. Aves namque   5
non sunt quas te credis cernere, sed signa summitatibus malorum
apposita. Sciasque procul dubio classem adventare hostilem jam
dudum a rege tuis subjugato viribus nos persecutum missam.
Forsitan quippe aliqua tempestate urgente, externam coacti sunt
petere regionem; quod usque ad presens sibi more causa exstitit.   10
Nunc vero suis votis aura favente redeunt. Militibus itaque
arma capere impera, nec nos adversarii inermes repperiant."

    Ad imperium igitur centurionis qui in illa nave habebantur
armantur; ceterisque carinis, nam xxx erant, xv scilicet quas
illo adduxit, et totidem quas a subacta insula prioribus   15
adjunxit; idem faciendi dant signa tibicines. Ordinantur que
a fronte que a dextra, vel leva hostes invadant, que eciam
quasi insidiando circumveniant. Quinque autem quas rostratas
habebat, in quarum prima ipse erat [31r,col.1] in fronte
constituit subito lintres advenientes aggresuras hostiles.   20
Hoc quidem navium genere piratici maxime navale exercentes
prelium utuntur, cuius vis tam immanis est, ut quamcumque ratem
impeterit, a summa usque ad inferiorem proscindat tabulam.

---

2. exercere MS: exercere solent, Bruce   4. autem: aut MS, Bruce.
23. proscindat: procindat MS, Bruce

Indeed it is said that with a storm imminent, these birds, wheeling about, now together, now separated, circle into mass flight and foretell by their behavior coming disaster."

The Knight of the Surcoat, however, standing by him at that moment and perceiving things as they really were, said, "Sir, your concept is in error. For those are not birds which you think you see but standards mounted on mastheads. You must realize that it is without doubt the enemy fleet approaching which was sent to pursue us some time ago by the king already subjugated by your forces. Perhaps they were driven by some storm and forced to seek a foreign harbor, the reason, it seems to me, for the delay. Now since the wind favors their plans, they have returned. Order the knights to put on their armor so the enemy will not find us unarmed."

At the command of the centurion, they who were aboard that ship armed themselves; and to the rest of the ships (for there were thirty, fifteen of which he had led there and just as many others he had acquired later from the conquered island) the ship's trumpets gave a signal to do the same. The ships were placed in battle order: some to attack the enemy from the front, others from the left or right, and still others to remain in the rear as a trap. Moreover, five ships that had rams, in the first of which he was himself, he ordered ahead to attack the advancing enemy vessels with sudden force. Those experienced in naval battle use this particular type of ship fully rigged for piracy, the armament of which is so strong that whatever ship it strikes, it rips the planking open from top to bottom.

Iccirco vero rostrate dicuntur, quod omne spacium inter proram
et carinam eminens ferro tegitur, cristam aduncis premunitam
ferreis habens in longitudine prori autem in vertice ferrea
gerunt capita, ad modum galli cristatis rostris munita.
Eriguntur quoque propugnacula, quibus viri imponuntur   5
fortissimi, inpungnancium impetum a summo refrenaturi saxis et
jaculis. Onerarie autem puppes retro locantur; ut si milite
instructe cederent, saltim vel ipse manus diripiencium
effugerent.

     Omnibus itaque ut expediebat dispositis jactatis   10
anchoris, adventum opperiebatur hostium. Jamque inimica classe
apparente, dictis Militis cum tunica armature visus fidem
prebebat.   Eumque insinuabat non falsum opinatum fuisse.
Catervatim et ipsi classem distinguunt, nec minori astucia
singula tali discrimini necessaria prevident. Miles autem cum   15
tunica armature, eos ad bella paratos appropinquare intuens,
chiulas confestim sublatis anchoris solui, ventisque vela
committens, ipsas remis jubet impelli; atque exercitu per trans-
tra et tabulata disposito, prior in liburnum quo dux hostium
vehebatur irruit. Cuius prorum [31r,col.2] una cum carina primo   20
confrigens impetu, inmodicum adusque malum ictum perduxit, quod
rostro impingente fractum undas compulit oppetere vertice.

14. ipsi: ipse MS, Bruce 16 paratos: petratos corrected in margin MS.
20. primo MS: omitted Bruce.

Because all the area projecting between the prow and keel is covered with iron, the ridge armed with iron hooks, the vertex of the extension of the ram carrying iron points and armed like the crested beak of the cock, these ships are termed "rostrated." Towers are also erected on which are stationed the strongest men ready to stop the impetus of the enemy defense by hurling stones and javelins from above. The merchant ships were placed toward the rear so that if the ships carrying knights yielded, these could withdraw and might at least escape the hands of the pillagers.

When everything necessary was done, dropping anchor, they awaited the coming of the enemy. The sighting of the hostile fleet brought quick confirmation to the words of the Knight of the Surcoat. What he had reasoned had not been false. The men observed for themselves the fleet in formation and foresaw with no less astuteness the tactics required for such a battle.

The Knight of the Surcoat, observing the pirates to be prepared for battle and closing, immediately ordered the anchors raised and, as soon as the sails caught the winds, the ships to be driven forward by oars. Armed men in place on deck and thwarts, he rushed the foremost galley on which the commander of the enemy fleet was sailing. The knight, smashing first with his single ship, drove home a blow by the force of its ram with such power all the way through to the mast that when the ram struck with its iron vertex, it forced the crippled vessel to seek the depths.

Assunt et alie rates Militi cum tunica armature presidio,
quassatamque navem circumdant et licet se strenue defensarent
repugnantes opprimunt.   E quibus quosdam involvunt fluctibus,
quosdam securibus obtruncant et gladiis.   Reliquam autem partem
vinclis edomant, atque viriliter pungnante ne vivus hostium   5
manibus incideret perempto principe; opes et exuvias diripiunt,
phaselumque pelago submergunt.

   Post horum autem perniciem Miles cun tunica armature
audacius in superstites progreditur.   A quibus cum clamore
conjunctis viribus exceptus, circumdatur, atque a suis secretus   10
quoquoversus valde inpugnatur.   Missilium jactu aera obfuscari,
eorumque multitudine freti superficiem operiri videres.   Hinc et
inde ingens caucium moles volvebatur, quorum strepitus non minus
horroris quam discriminis efficiebat.   Omni telorum instant
genere, ratem Militis cum tunica armature violare nitentes, sed   15
singule sibi tabule laminis incastrate ferreis nullius ictibus
solvebantur.   Licetque tantis hostium stiparetur cuneis, non
tamen minora patrabat quam paciebatur facinora.   Cuius ubi
hostes animadvertere pertinaciam, eumque malle mori quam vinci,
nec viribus eum posse submitti, nec cedere tutum instanti,   20
piram (ignem videlicet Grecum) eius in lintrem jaculati sunt.

---

11. jactu: jatu, corrected MS.

The other ships came up and surrounded the shattered vessel
as reinforcement for the Knight of the Surcoat, and even though
the enemy soldiers defended themselves vigorously, the knight's
men overcame those who resisted.   Some of them were thrown
overboard, others were cut down by battle-axes and swords.   5
Those remaining they restrained with chains.   They slew the
commander, who fought valiantly lest he fall living into the
hands of his enemy.   Then they seized the riches and arms and
sank the ship beneath the sea.

    After overthrowing these men, The Knight of the Surcoat   10
advanced even more daringly into the remaining ships.   With a
battlecry these ships regrouped; he was intercepted, surrounded,
cut off from his companions, and attacked fiercely from all
sides.   You could see the air darkened by the hurling of
javelins and the surface of the sea covered with their great   15
numbers.   From one side and the other, a huge piece of
stone-throwing ordnance was manipulated in a circular course,
the din of which produced no less horror than the danger.   The
contenders pressed with every kind of weapon trying to destroy
the ship of the Knight of the Surcoat, but the planking, each   20
board individually fastened with iron, did not separate from the
blows.   Hemmed in as he was by the formations of the enemy, he
still did more damage than he received.   When the enemy saw his
determination, that he preferred to die rather than be
conquered, nor could he be forced to submit nor lower his   25
defense for an instant, they hurled their fire, that is to say
"Greek fire," into the ship.

[31v,col.1] Diversis autem modis fit ignis huiusmodi. At cuius vis ad peragenda quibus adhibetur negocia, major pertinaciorque existit, hoc ordine conficitur. Hii quibus illum conficiendi pericia est, vas primitus aptant eneum, et quot volverint rubetas accipiunt, atque in eo carne 5 columbina et melle per iii menses alunt. Quo spacio completo, biduo vel triduo ipsos inpastos relictos, lacte proleque fete mammis alcuius bestie applicant. Cuius lac tam diu sugendo ebibunt donec ultro saturi decidant. Tumentes autem venenifero liquore, rogo subposito imponuntur 10 vasculo. Quibus et chelindri serpentes adhibentur aquatici quos denis ante diebus busto inclusos humanum paverit cadaver. Est et aspis venenifera atque mortifera tria uno in gutture gerens capita, cuius nomen menti excidit, animal venenosum, quicquid attigerit irremediabili peste corrumpens. Tellus 15 namque eius ad tactum herba et segete, unda piscibus, arbores destituuntur fructibus; et unde magis mirandum est, si vel minutissima stilla arborem cuiuslibet grossitudinis sit infecerit, more cancri corrodens, quo loco cederit per medium consumpto humi sternit. Nullam huic cladi medelam obesse posse 20 compertum est; quin homines et pecudes, si vel saltim cutis superficiem attigerit, in talia penetrans statim perimat.

---

6. iii: m MS, Bruce 8. bestie: marked to be deleted MS. 13. aspis: asspis MS, Bruce; venifera: venifa MS, Bruce 19. cederit MS, ceciderit, Bruce.

Fire of this kind may in fact be made in several ways. But the power of the formula that produces the fiercest fire and continues burning longest is prepared in this way. Those who possess the knowledge of preparation first make ready a brass vessel, and they collect poisonous toads of the kind called "rubetae," as many as needed, and they force-feed them with dove meat and honey for three months. After this period has elapsed, they allow the toads to fast for two or three days; then they put the little beasts to the teats of some prolific creature, recently delivered and lactating, whose milk they suck for such a long time that they fall off from complete satiety. Swollen by poisonous fluid, they are laid upon a small vessel, and a fire hot enough to consume them like a funeral pyre is set under it. To these also are added water snakes, "chelyndri," which for ten days preceding their inclusion on the pyre are fed on a human cadaver. There is in addition an asp (whose name escapes me), poisonous and deadly, bearing three heads upon one gullet, a venomous creature able to corrupt with incurable disease whatsoever it touches. At the touch of it the field loses its vegetation, the sea its fish, the trees their fruit, and so it is a very great marvel. Even if the most minute distillation infects a tree, no matter how huge, at that spot where it drops, it is absorbed inwardly, and like a chancre it will corrode, felling the tree to the earth. It has been learned that no remedy can stop the destruction; and even worse, if men or beasts are touched even slightly on the surface of the skin by this poison, it penetrates and they are slain instantly.

Vis cuius quanta sit e flamma eius ab ore evaporante maxime
[31v,col.2] potest perpendi, qua dum ipse majori estu uritur,
sepius quam inhabitat silva inflammatur. E sanie autem eius ab
triplici rictu profluente tres herbe gignuntur scilicet ex
singulis singule. Quarum primam siquis cibo vel potu sumpserit   5
mente mutata in rabiem vertitur; secunda una cum gustu se necem
infert gustanti; tercie vero succus, se potatum aut unctum,
regio morbo inficit. Hec autem ubi adoleverint gramina, infamis
ipsa si invenerit depascitur belva. Capta quoque antequam
prefato adhibeatur negocio, illarum per septimanam inpinguatur   10
pabulo. Fel quoque et testiculi lupi non desunt ambigui, qui
vento et aura progenitus, quicquid attigerit, tacte rei in se
figuram accipit. Calculus autem ligurius orbe in extremo
repertus non minimum inter cetera locum optinet, eadem qua et
ipse virtute preditus, e cuius concreta urina pervenire   15
creditur. Lincis namque nil obstat obtutibus, ut eciam cis
consistens materiam quid citra agatur certo contempletur lumine.
Capud eciam cor et jecur cornicis novena metite secula, horum
vires ad auctum adiciuntur. Sulphur autem pix et resina, oleum,
tartarum et bitumen, minime adimuntur predictis que quem   20
adhibite flamme cito fervorem corripiunt, sero deponunt.

11-19. cf. Ovid. Meta. 7.11.270-71; Pliny. Nat.Hist. 8.24,47.
9. belva: bellva corrected MS. 12. tacte: tecte corrected MS.
13. accipit: accepit corrected MS. 17. citra MS: ultra, Bruce
20. tartarum MS, cartarum Bruce.

How great its power is can be determined from the flame spewing intensely from the creature's mouth; and while it is itself burning with greatest heat, very often the forest it inhabits is set afire. From the venomous slaver that flows from its triple gaping mouths, three extracts are produced, doubtless a trace 5 from each. The first of these if consumed by anyone in meat or drink will drive him mad, derange his mind; the second also brings death to the taster with but a taste; the juice of the third infects with the king's evil by swallowing or rubbing it. This monstrous beast, if one comes upon it when the poisons are 10 fully developed, will destroy itself. If indeed it is captured, before it can be added to the above process, it must be fattened for a week on the proper food for these creatures. In addition there must be included the gall bladder and testicles of a wolf that does not lack the ability to change its nature, a creature 15 engendered by air and wind so that whatever it touches, by contact it receives that form. Also a "ligurius," obtained from the end of the earth, occupies no small place among the other ingredients, the same stone that is believed to be both endowed with virtue and to originate from the solidified urine of the 20 wolf. For nothing interrupts the concentrated staring of the lynx; even the inner matter which surely must be excreted hardens while it contemplates the light. Also the head, the heart, and the liver of a crow which has measured out its ninth generation are added to increase the strength of the formula. 25 Sulphur, also, and pitch, resin, olive oil, tartar, and petroleum are not in the least withheld from these things already mentioned; they feed the fire quickly when the flame is applied; they are set aside until later.

Hec igitur ubi collecta fuerint, quo retuli ordine cacabo
ex ere includuntur purissimo locataque usque ad hos vasis ruffi
hominis draconisque superfunduntur cruore. Sanguini quippe
[32r,col.1] ruffi ignea natura inesse creditur, quod et color
pili et que maxime in huiusmodi vigere solet, vivacitas patenter   5
ostendit ingenii. Juventus autem cui barba et cesaries ruffa
fuerit eiusdem coloris impetigines faciem asperserint, pulcro
inducitur thalamo, omniumque apparatu dapium, unius mensis
delicate impinguatur spacio. Singulis quoque diebus foco ante
eum accenso ad auctum sanguinem vino inebriatur, sed sedule a   10
femineis servatur amplexibus. Mense vero expleto, in medio
domus hinc et inde ad eius longitudinem igniti sternunter
carbones, inter quos ipse cibo potuque inpurgitatus depositis
indumentis exponitur; ac more veruum utroque in latere ad ignem
versatur. Sufficienter autem calefactus, jamque venis toto   15
turgentibus corpore fleobotomatur, scilicet, utriusque brachii
fibris ex transverso incisis. Interim vero dum sanguinem minuit
ad refocillandam mentem offas in vino accipit, ne, illa
debilitata vel in extasi rapta, liquor concrescatur optatus.
Tam diu autem sanguis effluere sinitur, donec eius defeccio   20
mortem inducens animam corpore eiciat. Et primum quidem cruore
draconis admixto per se calefit diutissime, dein ceteris
superfusus omnia simul confundit.

2. ex ere: exere MS, Bruce; hos MS: os Bruce. 3. Sanguini: Saguini MS,
Bruce 4. ruffi: ru/ruffi MS. 19. concrescatur: concreatur MS, Bruce

When these items have been collected in the order I have stated, they are enclosed in a heating vessel made of the purest bronze, and once they are in place, the vessel is filled to the brim with the blood of a red-haired man and a dragon. Indeed, a fiery nature is attributed to the blood of the red-haired man because of both the color of the hair and the great vigor these men usually have, a vivacity that openly attests their nature. A youth, then, whose beard and hair are red, with skin eruptions of the same color sprinkling his face, is led into a fine bedroom, and for the space of one month he is fattened sumptuously on every prepared delicacy. During this time, each day a hearth fire is kindled before him, and he is made drunk with wine in order to increase the blood; and he is carefully kept from the embraces of women. When the month has come to an end, in the middle of the room charcoal fires of a man's length are lighted; he is exposed between these when he is full of food and drink and his clothing is removed; in the way meat is turned on the spit, he is turned before the fire. Warmed sufficiently, the veins on his entire body soon become swollen, and he is bled, that is the veins of both arms are cut transversely. In the meantime, while he loses blood, he receives wafers in wine to sustain his spirit, lest because of weakness or a trance, the desired liquid be clotted. For a long time, then, the blood is allowed to flow, until it brings on death by its deficiency and casts the soul from the body. Next, having been mixed with the blood of the dragon, it is heated separately for a long time. Finally poured over the other substances, it blends the mixture together.

5

10

15

20

25

Si autem queritur quomodo draco prendatur, viri eliguntur
fortissimi qui prius eius qua latitat scrutentur [32r,col.2]
cavernam; inventaque per girum eius aditus soporifera gramina
variis sternunt aromatibus tincta. Quorum terre hiatum exiens
dum draco flagranciam sentit; ea avide consumens statim sopore 5
opprimitur, ac ab insidiantibus tuto in loco non eminus abditis
circumventus, obtruncatur. A quibus eius sanguis una cum gemma
draconcia asportatur, quam eius elisio excuciunt crebro, et hinc
multimodis adhibenda negociis.

Vas autem in quo hec confidencia sunt tripos est, cuius 10
ansata summitas artis preartatur faucibus cooperculum ex ere
habens. Quo dum clauditur ita sibi utrumque incastratur, ut nec
vel modicus vapor inde evaporet fumi. Omnibus vero illi
inpositis, ignis confestim supponitur atque vii continuis
diebus, totidemque noctibus pice naptaque flamme injectis ut 15
magis ferveat ebullitur. Fit quoque et virga aerea cuius
curvata summmitas ad modum clepsedre coaptatur, qua parvum
foramen quod in vasis cooperculi patet vertice vi prioribus
obturatur diebus. Septima autem die flamma in cacabo accensa,
inmanis strepitus, ac si terre motus fieret intro auditur, aut 20
si eminus positus ferventis pelagi aure murmura percipias.
Succense autem flamme ubi notum minister signum perceperit,
clepsedram exterius per acerrimo perfundit aceto; cuius
soliditatem penetrans jam nitentis erumpere flamme restringit
impetum. 25

---

5. flagranciam MS: fragranciam, Bruce 9. adhibenda MS: adhibenda [est], Bruce 11. faucibus: facibus corrected MS.
23. per acerrimo: per acerimo MS: peracerrimo, Bruce

If one is asked how a dragon may be caught, first stalwart
men are chosen to search out the dragon's cave, the den where
it lurks, and when they have found it, they sprinkle
sleep-inducing drugs moistened with various spices across the
rim of its entrance. When the dragon, leaving the mouth of the   5
cave, smells these fragrances, it consumes them voraciously and
is at once overcome by sleep. The men, who have been hidden in
a safe place not far away, surround the beast and slaughter it.
The men carry off the dragon blood, along with the dragon gem
that they shake loose by smashing its brain. The gem may then   10
be used in many sorts of undertakings.

The vessel in which these substances are placed is a
tripod whose handled upper section with its lid of bronze is
constructed to fit the narrow neck snugly. Closed by this, it
is so tightly fitted on all sides that not even the least wisp   15
of smoke escapes from it. When everything has been placed in
this vessel, fire is immediately kindled under it, and for seven
days and seven nights the flames are fed with pitch and naphtha
so that it will boil intensely. There is, in addition, a
copper tube, the uppermost end of which has been bent, that is   20
attached in the manner of a valve. By means of this a small
hole on top of the lid of the vessel is kept closed for the
first six days. On the seventh day, when the flame in the
heating vessel is ignited, a tremendous roar inside can be
heard, like an earthquake, or as if at a distance you heard the   25
rumblings of a raging sea. When the attendant has observed the
familiar signs of the ignited fire, he pours into the valve on
the outside some very sharp vinegar; penetrating its mass, it
checks the force of the fire now striving to burst out.

Folles autem quante suffecerint quibus [32v,col.1] ignis
abdatur parantur aenee, quarum incastrature ita sibi anfracte
compaginantur ut series hee flamma quam que e ligno et corio
fiunt venti penetrantur afflatu. Sed et adeo exstant tricabiles
ut magis e corio quam aere composita crederes. Flamma itaque   5
injecto aceto a suo fervore cohibita, clepsedra eximitur atque
ductilis calamus in folle preminens, foramini vasis apponitur.
Cuius attractu aure, ignis a cacabo exhauritur; statim ne exeat,
os calami clepsedra obturatur. Sic et in ceteris ignis
servandus recipitur. Pars vero parva in cacabo relinquitur, cui   10
cotidie fomes qua nutriatur adhibenda. Nec non et folium in
medio, ad modum fenestrule parva habentur foramina per que ne
extinguatur flamma alitur. Hoc ordine ignis Grecus paratur.
Quem quid valere si queris, nulla est tam fortis machina, nulla
tam magna carina ad quas, si jaculetur, quin latus utrumque   15
omnia consumens obstancia penetret. Nec ullo modo valet
extingui, donec materia quam consumat defecerit. Quodque magis
obstupendum est, eciam inter undas ardet, et si igni admisceatur
communi se semper uno in globo continens eundem velud lingna
depopulabitur.   20

---

4. tricabiles MS: tractabiles, Bruce   5. quam: quem MS, Bruce
19. velud lingna MS: velut ligna, Bruce.

Bellows are constructed of bronze, as many as suffice, by which the fire is drawn out; their connectors are screwed together so tightly that the series of connections is penetrated by the fire under the blast of air as though made of wood and leather. For they are indeed so meshed that you would more   5
easily believe them composed of leather than bronze. Once the fire has been moderated from its intense heat by the vinegar dousing, the valve is released and the ductile pipe projecting forward in the bellows is applied to the small opening of the vessel. By the suction of the air flow of this, the fire is   10
pumped out of the heating vessel. Immediately, lest the flames rise up, the mouth of the tube is closed by the valve. Thus the fire is received into other containers to be held for later use. A small part, it is true, is retained in the heating vessel; the heat by which it is nourished must be applied daily. Small   15
openings with a leaf in the middle like a small shutter are provided through which fuel is fed lest the flame go out. By this routine is Greek fire prepared. If you ask what power it has, no military machine is so strong, no ship so great but that if the fire is thrown it penetrates defenses and consumes   20
everything on every side. It has the strength to resist being extinguished by anyone until the matter that it consumes is exhausted. What is more astounding, it burns also among the waves; and if it is mingled with common fire, it will continue to hold itself in a separate fireball and will consume common   25
fire like wood.

77

Igitur ut superius dictum est, ubi hostes Militem cum
tunica armature armis invincibilem experti sunt, unus eorum
follem qua infaustus ignis serva[32v,col2]batur arripuit; atque
calamo dempta clepsedra, eius unam e tabulis leva deprimens
alteramque dextra elevans, eas ab invicem compressit conamine;   5
ignemque ejaculans, centurianam eo ratem iii remigantibus ustis
per medium penetrat. Nec mora tota flamma corripitur, unde non
parvus ei insidentibus metus incutitur. Interius quippe flamma
exterius septi hostibus quid agerent ignorabant; nec se
defensandi, nec ulciscendi dabatur copia. Si fuge vellent   10
consulere nec undis nec adversariis se tutum erat committere.
In navi autem remanentibus mors nihilominus intentabatur. Miles
autem cum tunica armature considerans rem nisi quantocius
succurreretur sibi ad irremediabile periculum vergere, omniaque
virtutis viriumque pensari examine; resumpto vigore, uni sibi   15
insistencium navi armatus insilit, et quosdam obtrunccans,
quosdam involvens fluctibus; socios triplici ereptos infortunio
scilicet flammarum globis, undarum naufragio, hostiumque furori,
illi transponit. Accriorique ira succensus, coadunata classe
protinus se ultum properat; denisque submersis, myoparontas   20
xxx[ta] hostium enervata virtute abducit.

---

15. resumpto: resupto MS, Bruce 21. myoparontas MS: myoparonas, Bruce

When the enemy had discovered by their efforts that the Knight of the Surcoat was unconquerable by arms, one of them seized the bellows in which the baleful fire was contained; and removing the valve from the tube, pressing down one of the boards with his left hand, and raising the other with his right,   5 he compressed them by turns with utmost exertion. With the flaming incendiary fuel streaming forward, he sprayed the centurion's galleon amidship, consuming four oarsmen with flames. Quickly everything was enveloped in fire and panic spread among the men on board. Surrounded by the flames within   10 and the enemy without, they did not know what to do; they had no power to defend themselves nor to attack. If they wanted to consider flight, neither to the waves nor to the enemy was it safe to commit themselves. Either way, death was imminent for those remaining on the ship. The Knight of the Surcoat,   15 considering the crisis--that without immediate help disaster beyond remedy hung over his men and that everything weighed in the balance of his strength and courage--drove himself forward with renewed determination. Alone, he leaped armed onto the ship of the attackers, cutting down some of the enemy, throwing   20 others to the waves. He delivered his companions across to the ship, rescuing them from a threefold bane: the balls of fire, the shipwrecking waves, and the fury of the enemy. Enraged with a more consuming fury, as soon as the fleet had again come together, he immediately avenged himself. After having sunk   25 every tenth ship and broken the enemy's power, he captured thirty of the pirate vessels.

Navali tandem non sine maximo discrimine confecto prelio,
quod reliquum erat itineris prospere peragunt, Jerosolimam
tempore statuto incolumes perveniunt. Qui incredibili cunctorum
favore suscepti, defatigata membra tum terre marisque operoso
itinere, cum multiplici periculorum [33r,col.1] et preliorum   5
discrimine, quiete et ocio delicacius et indulgencius
recrearunt. Ad quos interim valida bellatorum coadunantur
agmina, et a finitimis extraneisque princibus militum destinatur
copia. Jubent et ipsi per omnem regionem milites eligi urbes et
oppida locis opportunis firmis muris altisque turribus   10
circumdari viris fortissimis, omni telorum apparatu, re
frumentaria pabuloque sufficienti in expedicionem pugne muniri.
Fiebatque cotidie per diversas sanctorum memorias communis ab
universis ad Deum sedule oracio oracionique jejuniorum
elemosinarumque continuebatur devocio, ut sibi famulantibus   15
optatum conferret triumphum et adversarios maneret excidium.

        Prefixus interea dies duelli illuxerat, armatorum-
que Christianorum videlicet et paganorum utrimque innumera-
bilis exercitus consertis cuneis; duo ut pactum fuerat
armis septi agoniste certaturi in medio prodeunt.   20
Hinc Miles cum tunica armature cuius animi audacia,
virtus prolata, probitas assueta, vincendi consuetudo,
et justior causa, socios spe exhilarabat triumphi.

---

15. continuebatur MS: contuebat, Bruce

When, not without grave peril, the naval battle was
finally over, they completed the rest of the journey with good
fortune.   They arrived safely in Jerusalem at the appointed
time.   After being received with unbelievable acclaim by
everyone, the men--exhausted by the arduous journey by both   5
land and sea, a multiplicity of dangers and the hazard of
battles--restored their bodies with quiet rest and leisurely
care.   Meanwhile the mighty hosts of warriors had assembled, and
facilities were prepared for these men by the local and foreign
commanders of the knights.   They also ordered knights to be   10
chosen throughout the entire region, towns and cities in
suitable locations to be enclosed with strong walls and high
towers, and these to be put into a state of defense by the
strongest men, with all weapons ready and stores of provisions
and fodder adequate for siege.   Prayer was offered daily to God   15
by all the people through various relics of the saints, and
devotion to prayer with fasting and almsgiving was continued so
that He might confer the desired triumph to those who served
Him, and that destruction would await the adversary.

   The day dawned that had been set for the duel, and   20
when the vast army of armored Christians and, of course,
pagans had been drawn up in formation on either side, the
two men who were to render judgment by combat, sheathed in
armor, proceeded according to the agreement to the center.
Here the Knight of the Surcoat, by boldness of spirit, proven   25
courage, accustomed prowess, habit of winning, and the more
righteous cause, filled his allies with the hope of victory.

Alius autem partis adverse Gormundi vocabolo procera membra, inmanis statura, truculenta facies, bellorum frequencia, singularis omnium estimata fortitudo, armorum horror et strepitus sibi cessurum spondere videbantur tropheum. Pedites vero uterque processerunt: quia ob eius inmoderatam altitudinem   5 nullus equus Gormundum ad[33r.col.2]mittere sessorem valebat. Objectis igitur clipeis collatisque dextris audaciter adinvicem congrediuntur; et quantum vis suppetit, quantasque ira vires administrat, alter alterum stricto mucrone impetit. Mille ictus ingeminant; milleque modis mutue cedi mutuisque insistunt   10 vulneribus. Feriunt et feriuntur, pellunt et propelluntur; rotaque fortune vario casu inter eos versatur. Nil quid virtutis et fortitudinis sit prossus relinquitur, cunctorumque obtutus in eos infiguntur. Quis promcior ad feriendum fortiorve ad paciundum ignoratur; inter quos tam crebri ictus, tamque graves   15 sine temporis inter capedine dividebantur colaphi, ut quis daret vel acciperet, difficile posset adverti. Uter viribus pocior haberetur nescires; dum quo magis pungne insisterent eo valencioribus animis ad certamen inhiarent. Modo lepidis cavillacionibus suos ictus interserunt, modo cynedis salibus   20 suorum vicissim mentes exasperant; modo haneli se retrahunt, modo aura concepta recreati acriores concurrent. Recreatisque viribus, fervenciori impetu copulantur, et quasi ab eis nichil antea actum sit effere mentes efferacius debachantur.

---

15. paciundum MS: paciendum, Bruce 20. cynedis MS: cinedis, Bruce
21. haneli MS: anheli, Bruce retrahunt: retrahuntur MS, Bruce

His opponent Gormundus, because of his remarkable limbs, huge
stature, cruel face, war experience, notable courage as attested
by all, and the horror and din of his weapons, seemed to promise
that triumph would be accorded to him. Both of them came on
foot; because of his immense height Gormundus could find no   5
horse strong enough to bear him.

　　With shields opposed and right arms raised, they both join
boldly in mutual attack. However much strength each has and
however great the force that anger directs, each seeks the other
with naked blade. A thousand thrusts are returned and in a   10
thousand ways they press on with their exchange of bloodletting
and wounds. They strike and are stricken; they advance and are
driven back. The wheel of fortune turns between them with
various effects. Nothing whatever is omitted that may be summed
up in courage and strength; everyone's eyes are fixed on them.   15
If either one is more prepared for dealing death and either
braver in endurance, it is not known; between these men such
frequent thrusts and severe blows are unceasingly exchanged that
who gives and who receives them is hard to discern. You cannot
tell which man is of greater strength. The more they press the   20
fight, the more they hunger for battle. At times they
intersperse their blows with clever raillery; at times they
inflame each other with witty obscenities. Now they withdraw
out of breath; again refreshed they more eagerly rush together,
their wind regained. With renewed strength they join in a more   25
heated attack; and as if nothing had yet been done fiercely,
their spirits rage with still greater ferocity.

Videres eos sic confictando adversum se consistere quemadmodum
duos apros ferocissimos in singulari certamine qui nunc adunco
dente se obliquo ictu impetunt, nunc latera collidunt, nunc
pedes pedibus proterunt, quorum rictus interim modo fumida spuma
oblinit; modo ignis erumpens ignescit. [33v,col.1] Altero   5
siquidem virilius instante hic cedens longius propellitur;
russus isto prevalente ille retrogradi cogitur.   Hic quasi
insidiando vulnus inferre molitur.   Ille si quid ensis pateat
acumini sedule rimatur, sed alter conamen alterius haud impari
calliditate deludit et cassat.   Armorum quoque fragor longius   10
perstrepit, eorumque soliditas mucronum aciem hebetat et
retundit.   Ex quorum eciam collisione flamma crebrius prosiluit,
et ob inmoderatum laborem salsus per omnes artus a vertice usque
ad plantas sudor decurrit.   Incertumque erat cui victoria
cederet, dum utrorumque vires quisque equales pensaret.   Mira   15
igitur virtute miraque probitate, ea die abiit et pungnatum est,
certamineque ab hora diei, prima usque ad occiduum protracto,
nil actum est; quo vel alter preferreretur alteri, aut palma
ascriberetur aliqui.   Vesperascente itaque vulnerum, penitus
expertes segregantur; iterum in crastinum pungnaturi, iterumque   20
luctamen ex integro iniciaturi.

1. confictando MS: conflictanco, Bruce 4. proterunt: poterunt MS,
Bruce 16. abiit et MS: ab utroque, Bruce

You could see them stand facing each other like two ferocious boars in mortal combat who now attack each other with curved tusks in sidelong slashes, now strike their flanks, now trample hoof under hoof; their jaws now foam smoky spume, now spark forth fire. If one presses more violently, the other, yielding, is forced back; again the other prevailing, the first is forced to retreat. This one, as if setting a trap, strives to inflict a wound. The other, if anything lies open to the point of his sword, skillfully makes a thrust; but the first, with equal skill, mocks the other's effort and blocks it. The clash of arms echoes loudly far and wide, and the density of the armor blunts and dulls the sharp blades. From the striking of the arms sparks leap up. Because of the intense effort salty sweat pours off their limbs from top to toe.

It was uncertain to whom victory would fall; everyone thought that the strength of the two was matched. With remarkable courage and remarkable prowess on this day the fight had been fought and finished; from the first hour till sunset, nothing during the fighting was accomplished to give preference to one over the other or to ascribe the palm to either. So when the evening fell they were drawn apart with no deep wounds. In the morning they would fight again, and again the struggle would begin from the beginning.

85

Aurora vero oriente, bifaria acie galeate phalanges conveniunt, suosque luctatores in harenam producunt. Concurritur, conclamatur; in alterius necem quique grassatur. Iteratur pungna majori certamine, quia quo magis virtutem fuerat alter expertus alterius; eo se contra caucius agebat et forcius. 5 Pudebatque se vel ad modicum sibi alterutro cedere [33v,col.2] quos equi roboris omnium arbitrio constabat comprobatos fuisse. Quorum si ea die conflictum te contigisset aspicere eos hesterna jurares lusisse. Maximaque admiracione obstupesceres, quomodo ad tam crebros ictus ad tam graves colaphos, vel mucronum acumen 10 sine obtusione durare vel armorum soliditas inviolata manere, aut certe ipsi infessi insauciique tam diu quivissent subsistere. Eo quippe vigore, eoque valore gladii galeis infligebantur, clipeis contundebantur, ut ex scintillis prorumpentibus aera choruscarent sibique collisum calebs 15 calibem repelleret, dissilentemque in eum a quo vibrabatur retorqueret. Crebris afflatibus aera vexant, pila pilis et ictus ictibus obicientes. Unanimiter insistunt, pugnam acerrimam ingerunt; ardoremque pugnandi prelia protracta conferunt. Pectora pectoribus protendunt, omnique nisu 20 invadere et resistere nituntur. Audaciam unius animositas alterius provocat, et pertinacia illius, huius animi tenorem strenuiorem reddebat. Alternis viribus alterna virtus fomenta prebebat, et utriusque vigor se metitus ex altero proficiebat.

---

9. admiracione: admiraccione MS, Bruce 10. colaphos: calaphos MS, Bruce 15. collisum: collisam MS, Bruce; calebs calibem MS: chalybs chalybem, Bruce 16. vibratur: viblatur MS, vibrabatur, Bruce 19. ardoremque MS: ardorempue, Bruce 22. pertinacia: pertinaciam MS, Bruce

At Aurora's rising the helmeted phalanxes came together in a two-fold battle line, and the contending factions led their men to the arena. They clashed, there was a shout, each man intended to inflict death on the other. The man-to-man fight was repeated with greater rivalry because the more one made   5
trial of the daring of the other, the more the other conducted himself with care and bravery. It was a source of shame that men who in everyone's judgment were definitely proven to be of equal strength should yield in the smallest degree. For if on that day you had watched the battle of these two, you would have   10
sworn that they had merely played the day before. With the greatest admiration you would have been astounded, considering such repeated blows, such severe buffets, how the keenness of the sword blades could have lasted without dulling, how the solidity of the armor could have remained inviolate, and   15
particularly how they themselves, unwearied and uninjured, could have stood as long as they desired. Indeed with such vigor and such bravery did the swords clash against helmets and pound against shields that the air glowed with bursting sparks, and steel repelled clashed steel and sprang back at the one who had   20
wielded it.

      With frequent gasps they agitate the air, throwing weapon against weapon, blow upon blow. With one mind they stand; they wage a valiant fight, and the prolonged battle produces a lust for conflict. Chest expands to chest, and they strive with   25
every effort to attack and to resist. The boldness of one provokes the wrath of the other; and the stubbornness of that one increases a bolder intensity in this one. Each man's strength offers stimulus to the other's courage; and the vigor of one advances as it is matched by the other.   30

Plurimum autem diei pari fortuna inter eos expensum est, donec
Miles cum tunica armature, quiddam callide machinatus, dum se
Gormundum super levum genu fingeret velle percutere, et
Gormundus eo loco eream peltam opponerat; ipse dextra ad dextram
altius [34r,col.1] conversa ei ore in medio quod nudum patebat   5
ensis cuspidem inopinate ingessit iiii[or] que prioribus extusis
dentibus ei levam confregit maxillam. Leve tamen vulnus erat,
et quod pocius ad irritamentum furoris, quam ad doloris stimulos
illatum videretur, ut saucii vires quam incolumis ampliori
insania fervescerent. Gormundus itaque furore cum inflixo   10
concepto vulnere et more se dementis agens, nil exclamat
ulterius viribus parcendum est. Ut fera igitur bellva in
Militem cum tunica armature insurgit; brachioque in sullimi
erecto, tanta fortitudine scuto macheram inpressit, ut ordo
gemmarum insertus frustratim conquassatus difflueret, umbonem   15
avelleret, summitatemque clipei usque ad sanguinis effusionem
eius fronti illideret. Sevior et Miles cum tunica armature eum
excipit, sevitiaque dupplicata sevius res agitur, jamque negocium ad discrimen vergitur. Miles autem cum tunica armature
nactus locum in inmunitum hostis latus stricto mucrone irruit.   20
Sed Gormundo ictum callente et evitante, dum eius conatus cas-
satur ensis ab objecto egide exceptus scapulo tenus abrumpitur.

---

9. quam: added Bruce. 16. effusionem MS: effusionemque, Bruce
18. sevitiaque MS: seviciaque, Bruce.

88

Most of the day the odds between them were considered equal until the Knight of the Surcoat contrived a particular feint: that while he pretended he wanted to cut down Gormundus at a point above the left knee and drew Gormundus to oppose his bronze shield low, with his right hand turned to the right of 5 the other, the sword unexpectedly struck into the middle of Gormundus' mouth, which was unprotected, knocked out four front teeth, and broke the jawbone on the left side. The wound was not grave, and it seemed to act more powerfully as a goad to fury than as an incitement to despair, as the strength of a 10 wounded man may seethe with more fury than that of one unharmed. Enraged by the wound inflicted, Gormundus, acting demented, shouted no more words; he had to conserve his strength. Like a wild beast he lunged at the Knight of the Surcoat, and with his right arm high he slammed his sword on the 15 shield with such force that the row of set jewels, sharply jarred, flew piecemeal in different directions, the boss tore off, and the upper edge of the shield hit the knight's forehead hard enough to cause an effusion of blood.

More enraged, the Knight of the Surcoat again drew 20 him out, and with redoubled savagery, the contest was pressed more fiercely till the duel reached a crisis. The Knight of the Surcoat, seeking a weak spot, ran with sword raised at the unprotected flank of his enemy. But since Gormundus was experienced and parried the thrust, when the 25 knight pressed his effort, his sword was caught by the blocking of the shield and broke off down to the small shaft.

Nec eris soliditas duriciave ictus inmensitatem ferre potuit;
quin erea parma Gormundi contrita, per mediumque sub umbone
confracta minutas dissileret in partes. Universi ex hoc
confestim exercitus clamor inmensus exoritur, hinc merencium
illinc insultancium. Majus quippe discriminis [34r,col.2]   5
Militi cum tunica armature incumbebat cui vel quo se defensaret,
aut a se hostem abigeret, ense colliso nil prossus aderat.
Gormundo autem licet clipeum obvenisset comminui, mucro tamen
integer habebatur, cuius rigida ancipitique acie adversarii sui
tempora sine intermissione contundebat. Miles vero cum tunica   10
armature adversus eius impetus clipeum quoquoversus callide
pretendebat; sed nisi cicius Phebus occidens finem bello
posuisset, maxima procul dubio dispendia incurrisset. Meta
etenim assignata fuerat, quam mox ubi occidentis solis umbra
attigisset, omni occasione dilacioneque postposita, eos   15
segregari debere ratum manebat. Umbra igitur metam attingente,
invitis paganis et se vix a sedicione continentibus, dirimuntur
quodque duelli restabat diem in posterum protelatur.

    Noctis opaca solare jubar fugaverat, et conglomeratis
e diverso agminibus; campigeni se stagmati renovatis armis   20
truculenti ingerunt. Perosum quippe et pene exiciale
litigium inter utrumque exercitum exorsum fuerat, utrum
Militi cum tunica armature gladius, Gormundus clipeus, aut
utrique vel neutri, seu certe uni et non alteri, concederetur.

9. rigida: regida MS, Bruce 10. tempora: timpora MS, Bruce
12. pretendebat MS: protendebat, Bruce 15. dilacioneque:
dilaconeque MS, Bruce 20. stagmati MS: stagnati, Bruce

Neither the density nor the resistance of the metal was able to withstand the force of that blow, with the result that the bronze shield of Gormundus was smashed through the middle, and splitting under the boss, flew into pieces.

At this a great shout immediately rose from all the 5 assembled armies, cheers from one side, from the other insults. The greater danger to the Knight of the Surcoat was apparent: since his sword was shattered, nothing at all was at hand by which he could defend himself or by his own effort keep the enemy at bay. For Gormundus, although his shield was smashed, 10 his blade was intact; he was pounding his adversary with the rigid two-edged sword without a moment's pause. The Knight of the Surcoat, then, faced the attack and was skillfully presenting his shield in every direction. Yet if the setting of the sun had not quickly ended the duel, he would without doubt 15 have incurred the most severe loss. The end of the match had been determined so that at the time the shadow of the setting sun reached a set mark, it fulfilled the agreement that the men were to be separated, without regard to advantage or disadvantage. The shadow reached the mark then, and although 20 the pagans were unwilling and barely held themselves from revolt, the two combatants were in fact separated. Whatever remained of the fight would be postponed till the next day.

When the radiance of the sun had put to flight the darkness of the night, the lines from both sides assembled, and 25 the seasoned warriors presented themselves strengthened and grim, with arms repaired. A bitter, almost fatal quarrel arose between the two armies over whether the sword should be conceded to the Knight of the Surcoat or the shield to Gormundus, or to both, to neither, or to one and not the other. 30

Super qua re dissensione diu habita, magnisque altercacionibus
ventilata, omnium in hoc tandem convenit assensus equum fore;
ambobus annui quia nec iste sine ense se defendere nec ille
eliso clipeo, ab hostili erupcione [34v,col.1] se valebat
protegere. Ordinatis igitur ut caraxatum est utrimque nodis   5
peditum, et turmis equitum, ceterorumque armatorum, conferta
multitudine, duelligeri loricis crispantes, galeis cristati,
visu horrendi, stadium petunt, aleam belli ineunt, sese ad
pungnam lacessunt manuque prevalida invadunt et assiliunt. Nec
mora, tonitrus belli intonuit, offensio armorum perstrepuit,   10
sonitus ictuum efferbuit, et ignita collisio terribiliter
excanduit. Preduro ludo res agitur; dumque sagacius pungnant,
obstinacius perseverant. Tinnitu horribili aer resultat et
resonat; aereque percusso, montium concava stridorem
multiplicant. Horrenda belli facies, nulla quies fessis,   15
nulla respiracio dabatur hanelis. Omnimodis insistunt,
omnimodis operam adhibent ut eorum alter aut succumbat,
aut victoria pociatur. Nec estuantis solis fervor impedivit,
nec jugis labor vel decertacio obfuit; quin semper procaciores
insisterent seque mutuo semper inexsuperabiliores offenderent.   20
Atque sub armis facientes audacia animabantur, annimositateque
recreabantur. Horum si spectaculo assisteres, Laphitarum
pungna tibi in mente occurreret, qui quociens ictus ingemina-
bant, tociens Ciclopum incudes malleis contundi crederes.

9. lacessunt: lacescunt MS, Bruce   13. Tinnitu: Iinnitu, corrected
MS. 16. nulla: added, Bruce. 16. hanelis MS: anhelis, Bruce
23. mente MS: mentem, Bruce 24. Ciclopum MS: Ciclopem, Bruce
22-24. cf. Ps.-Callisthenes. Alex. 59.1.

After the dispute over this matter had continued for some time, and the main disagreements had been aired, the consensus of all was that the combatants should be made equal; both sides agreed that neither could this man defend himself without a sword, nor could that one, his shield destroyed, be strong 5 enough to protect himself from the attack of the adversary.

When the multitude was assembled, the platoons of foot, squadrons of horse and other armored men having been set in order as it was staked out on one side and the other, the duel-bearers--protected by loricas and crested helmets, 10 horrible to see--once again sought the stadium, began the gamble of combat, challenged each other to the fight, and attacked and assailed with powerful hands. At once the thunder of battle arose, the clash of arms rang out, the sound of blows increased, and the fiery shock grew fearfully hot. Battle is waged in a 15 fierce match; while they fight more knowingly, they persevere more boldly. The air rebounds and resounds with terrible noise, and as the bronze is struck the hollows of the mountains re-echo the noise. As the duel was by its nature dreadful, no rest was given to the weary nor breathing space allowed for the winded. 20 They endured by every means, and by every means they pursued the effort until one should fall and the other achieve the victory. Neither the heat of the summer sun nor the continuous strain hindered them, yet always the decision of the dispute was put off, for they resisted still more boldly, each one throwing 25 himself against the ever more unconquerable other. Thus the participants were inspired by daring under arms and they were invigorated by animosity. If you had seen the spectacle of these men, the fight of the Lapiths would come to your mind; as often as they repeated blows, that often you would have believed 30 you were witnessing the Cyclops' anvils beaten with hammers.

Cumque plurimum diei transisset, cepit Gormundus tum estu, tum
hostis assidua vexacione [34v,col.2] estuari aggravataque est
pungna in eum vehementer, totumque honus prelii ei incubuit.
Animo igitur dilitescebat, ac segnius et invalidius agebat.
Sensimque se subtrahens inpugnanti cedebat, nec ea qua ante   5
virtute vel se tuebatur; haud hostem aggrediebatur. Quod Miles
cum tunica armature advertens instancius instabat, anxiumque
spiritum illius anxiorem reddebat.   Nec destitit donec extra
circuli quo cingebantur limitem eum propelleret. Hic tumultus
et gemitus, ululatus et planctus incredule gentis ad sidera   10
tollitur; catervatimque mesti ad eum proclamabant, "Gormunde,
regredere; Gormunde, regredere! quid agis?   Quo refugis, miles
egregie?   Fugare, non fugere, tibi hactenus moris extitit.
Regredere! Proh dolor, regredere! Ne in ultimo dedecus omnia
ante dare gesta facinora obnubilet.   Fuge hic locus non est;   15
vinci aut vincere hic necessarium est." Ad quorum voces
Gormundus, pudore consternatus paulumque respirans et animatus,
forcius gressum fixit, infestantem adversarium viriliter abegit.
Vibransque gladium eiusmodi ictum intulit, quo complicatis
membris eum succumbere, ac mole ictus genuflexo, terram compel-   20
leret petere. Verum thorax inpenetrabilis mansit. Tunc Miles
cum tunica armature mente nimium efferatus concitus se erexit,
totus infremuit, sese in armis collegit, dextram [35r,col.1]
excussit, ac "Hic ictus," exclamat, "nostrum ludum dirimet."

---

6. haud: aud MS; aut, Bruce   10. planctus: plactus MS, Bruce
13-16. cf. Geof. Historia. 1.12.   15. dare MS, bene, Bruce
19. vibransque: vibranque, corrected MS.   24. hic ictus: hictus
MS with hic in margin, Bruce

94

When most of the day had passed, Gormundus began to waver from the heat and also from the constant harrying of his adversary. The attack was increased against him vehemently, and the whole weight of the clash fell on him. He weakened in spirit and fought less readily and effectively. Perceptibly drawing back from the battling knight, he retreated, nor did he defend himself with such courage as before; by no means was he pressing his opponent. And the Knight of the Surcoat, aware of this, stood his ground more boldly and caused the anxious man's spirit more anxiety. He did not stop till he had pushed him beyond the boundary of the circle which surrounded them.

Here the noise and murmurs, the shouts and screams of the incredulous people rose to the stars, and dismayed groups shouted to him, "Back, Gormundus, come back, Gormundus! What are you trying to do? Where do you think you are going, great knight? Running them off--not running--has always been your style. Come back, or in the end shame will erase all the winning you have ever done. This is not where you can run away. Here you must either win or die."

At these shouts, Gormundus, overcome by shame and gasping somewhat, took his stand more bravely and received the charge of his adversary more manfully. Brandishing the sword, he rendered such a blow that he felled the knight, legs folding under him; he forced him to the ground on his knees by the might of the thrust. But his cuirass remained impenetrable.

Then the Knight of the Surcoat, wild and enraged, sprung to his feet uninjured, drew himself up in his armor, brandished his right arm and screamed, "Here is the blow that ends the game!"

Summitatique eius cassidis ancipitem rumphee aciem imprimens,
jam armis calefactis, et ob hoc non resistentibus usque ad imum
pectus, omnia comminuens, confringens, et penetrans, ictum
conduxit (non optabile stomacho antidotum). Ac ensem vulneri
eximens, duas sectum in partes capud abscidit, cerebroque   5
effluente victor pede eminus a se pepulit. Quo superato et
crudeliter trucidato, pagani cum interminabili merore ultimum
super eo questum et luctum continuarunt, jamque armis correptis
ob eius ulcionem in Militem cum tunica armature irruissent, nisi
sanctitis inter se vetarentur legibus.   10

Per se igitur suo propungnatore neci dedito, juxta
condictas condiciones federis Romane se dicioni dedere, paceque
firmata, et obsidibus datis multa quoque vectigalium imposita ad
propria confusi remearunt. Miles vero cum tunica armature
splendide et victoriosissime adeptus tropheum, multisque ab   15
obtimatibus Jerosolimitanis honoratus muneribus Romam mature
rediit, triumphalique pompa ab imperatore et senatu susceptus
est. Quem imperatore in numero familiarium suorum decernens
quoad primum locum repperisset, eum summo sullimare honore
meritaque destinavit dignitate donare.   20

Hiis ita gestis nulloque contra Ro[35r,col.2]manum imperium arma presumente movere, Miles cum tunica armature pacem
fastiditus, miliciamque qua sua virtus et probitas exerceretur
semper affectans, studiose querere cepit quenam regio belli
tumultibus turbaretur. Cui dum famosum nomen Arturi sui   25

---

1. rumphee MS: romphee, Bruce 8. questum: questrum MS, Bruce
10. sanctitis MS: sanctis, Bruce

96

Striking with the double-edged sword down on top of the helmet while the armor was hot and and thus less resistant, he guided the blow, fracturing, splintering, and penetrating everything all the way to the breastbone. (Hardly a desirable stomach remedy!) When he freed the sword from the wound, the   5
skull split into two parts with the brains oozing out.   The victor kicked it away with his foot. When they saw their champion vanquished and slaughtered cruelly, the pagans united in the grief of death, mourning over him with interminable wailing; and presently when they had gathered up his armor, they   10
would have attacked the Knight of the Surcoat in vengeance, had they not been restrained by their inviolable laws.

Once their defender had been given over to death, the pagans yielded to the sovereignty of the pact with the Romans according to the agreed conditions: peace confirmed, hostages   15
given, heavy reparations imposed.   The enemy retired in confusion to their own country.   The Knight of the Surcoat, after he had been awarded the trophy for the brilliant and most supreme victory, and the highborn Jerusalemites had honored him with many rewards, in the fullness of time returned to Rome. He   20
was received by the emperor and the Senate with a triumphal procession.   The emperor, restoring him to the company of his closest companions where he had been before, resolved to raise him by the highest honor earned and to grant him high rank.

Once these deeds had been accomplished, as no one was   25
presuming to move against the Roman Empire by sword, the Knight of the Surcoat, disdaining the peaceful life and desiring military action where his courage and prowess could be constantly exercised, eagerly inquired what region might be torn by the tumults of war. When the name of Arthur, the famous   30

avunculi regis Britannie, nec tamen sibi noti, eiusque insignia
rerum gesta que jam toto orbe divulgabantur relata fuissent,
parvipendens universa que sibi ab imperatore conferebatur sepe,
sepiusque suppliciter flagitavit. Ac imperator quamquam eum ad
condignum promovere apicem jam proposuerat tantique viri   5
discessus sibi dampno fore non dubitaret, ut tamen a quibus
originem duceret scire valeret, nec non et per eum se regnum
Britannie, quod a Romanis diu discederat, adepturum confidens,
annuit quot petivit. Opulenta igitur preclara et preciosa ei
donaria largitus est, thecamque qua ipsius generis continebantur 10
indicia regi Arturo preferenda tradidit, adjunctis suis apicibus
quibus testabatur omnia que carte monimenta dicebant rata et
firma constare. Vetuitque ne loculum inspiceret antequam ad
regem Arturum venisset. Mandavit eciam primatibus Gallie per
quos transsiturus erat ut eum honorifice susciperent, servirent,   15
necessaria ei ministrarent, et per fines suos usque occeanum
salvum deducerent. Sicque valedicto, discessit rege relicto.

    Miles itaque cum tunica armature omnibus eius [35v,col.1]
discessum graviter ferentibus propositum iter arripuit,
Alpes transsiit, Galliasque transgressus Britanniam incolumis   20
attigit. Cui quo eo tempore rex Arturus degeret percuntanti
responsum est, eum apud Carlegion urbem in Demecia perhendin-
are, quam pre ceteris civitatibus frequentare consueverat.

---

3. conferebatur: added margin MS. 4. flagitavit: flatigavit MS, Bruce
6. discessus: discensus MS, Bruce   20. Alpes: Ales MS, corrected
in margin.

King of Britannia (his uncle, though he did not know it),
acclaimed for prowess around the world, was brought to his
attention, unmoved by all the emperor had given him, the Knight
of the Surcoat humbly petitioned [to leave] time and again. The
emperor, though he had already decided to promote him to the   5
highest position, and he had no doubt that the departure of so
worthy a man would be to his own loss, gave assent to the
petition in order that the knight might learn from whom he
traced his lineage, and also because he felt confident that
through him the Kingdom of Britannia, so long separated from the   10
Roman Empire, would be regained for himself. The emperor
bestowed on him rich, sumptuous, and priceless gifts and
delivered to him the coffer in which the proof of his parentage
remained, with orders that it must be presented to King Arthur,
adding his own letter as testimony that everything the documents   15
of record stated was established and confirmed. Further, he
forbade him to look inside the coffer before he entered the
presence of King Arthur. He ordered, then, that the first
citizens of the Gauls through whose lands the knight must pass
should receive him with honor, serve him, provide him with   20
necessities, and escort him safely through their territories all
the way to the sea. So, farewells spoken, the knight departed,
leaving the ruler behind.

   With everyone grieving over his departure, the Knight
of the Surcoat began the journey as planned. He crossed   25
the Alps; and having made his way through Gaul, he arrived
safely in Britannia. Inquiring where at that time King
Arthur was in residence, he learned that he was staying
at the city of Caerleon in Demetia, where he was accustomed
to spend more of his time than in his other cities.   30

99

Illa quippe nemoribus consita, feris fecunda, opibus opulenta, pratorum viriditate amena et irragacione fluminum Usce scilicet et Sabrine decora gratissimum penes se habitandi locum prebebat. Illic metropolis habebatur Demecie, illic legiones Romanorum hiemare solebant, illic Rex Arturus festa celebrabat solempnia   5
diademate insigniebatur, universe primorum Britannie ad eum conventus coadunabantur. Quo Arturum manere Miles cum tunica armature cognito, illo viam direxit; illo nec die nec nocte labori indulgens, properare animo intendit. Dum autem quadam nocte in cuius sequenti die ad Urbem Legionum perventurus erat   10
pergeret; inopina et inmanis procella visque ventorum cum pluvia apud Usce oppidum quod ab urbe vi miliariis distabat ei ingruit, cuius nimietate omnes ipsius socii aut deviarent, aut eum prosequi nequirent.

Eadem autem nocte rex Arturus cum sua conjuge regina   15
Gwendoloena thoro recubans, quia ob noctis diuturnitatem sibi sompnus erat fastidio; de multis adinvicem [35v,col.2] sermocinabantur. Erat quidem Gwendoloena regina cunctarum feminarum pulcherrima, sed veneficiis imbuta ut multociens ex sius sortilegiis communicaretur futura. Inter ceteras igitur cum rege   20
confabulaciones, "Domine," ait," tu te de tua probitate nimium gloriaris et extollis, neminemque tibi viribus parem existimas."

1-7. cf. Geof. Historia 3.189-93; 9.11.   2. Usce: Osce MS
3. prebebat: prebeat MS, corrected in margin.   4. Demecie:
Demicie MS, Bruce   5. celebrabat: celebrat, corrected MS
19. pulcherrima: pulcherima MS, Bruce

That charming city, laid out with groves, abounding in animals, rich in treasures, pleasant for its green meadows, and watered by the Usk River and, not far away, the Severn, offered a dwelling place of the utmost delight. Here was the metropolitan city of the province of Demetia, here the legions of Rome 5 used to spend the winters, here King Arthur celebrated the high feasts, wore the crown, and convened all the princes of Britannia for his assembly. As soon as the knight found out where Arthur was residing, he made his way in that direction, traveling swiftly in high spirits, pressing on day and night 10 without a break. He was almost there; it was the last night before he expected to reach Caerleon, and he was just outside the town of Usk,* six miles away, when a sudden violent storm struck with driving rain. Everyone with him either left the high road or was unable to keep up. 15

The same night, King Arthur and Gwendoloena, his queen, were talking to each other about many things while resting in bed. (Because of the length of night they had had enough sleep.) Queen Gwendoloena was indeed the most beautiful of all women, but she was initiated into sorcery, so that often from her 20 divinations she would read the future.

Among the other things she discussed with the king, she said, "Lord, you boast and greatly extol your prowess, and you assume that no one is your equal in strength."

Arturus, "Ita est," ait, "nonne et tui animus idem de me
sentit?" Regina, "Nempe hac ipsa noctis hora quidam miles e
Roma veniens per Usce municipium huc cursum tendit, quem virtute
et fortitudine tibi eminere ne dubites. Sonipedi residet cui
vigore, valore, decoreve alter equiparari non poterit. Arma ei   5
sunt impenetrabilia; nec est qui ad ferientis dextram subsistat.
Et ne me frivola arbitreris asserere, signum rei habeto quod
anulum aureum et iii myriadas cum equis duobus eum mihi summo
mane missurum tibi prenuncio." Arturus autem eam se nunquam in
huiusmodi presagiis fefellisse recogitans rem probare ea tamen   10
ignorante statuit. Consuetudinis enim habebat quod statim ubi
aliquem strenuum virum advenire audisset; se illi obvium daret,
ut mutuus congressus validiorem ostenderet.

      Paulo ergo post regina sopita surrexit, cornipedem
armatus ascendit, abiit Kaium tantummodo suum dapiferum   15
vie habens comitem. Occurrit Militi cum tunica armature
ad quendam rivulum pluvi[36r,col.1]alibus undis inundatum
subsistenti juxta quem vadi querens transitum, moram
parum verberat. Tetra quippe noctis deceptus caligne
profundi fluminis alveum autumaverat. Quem Arturus ex armorum   20
splendore animadvertens, "Cuias es, " exclamat, "qui hanc
noctis silencio oberas patriam? Exulne es, predo an insidiator?"

---

20. autumaverat: autumarat MS 22. oberas MS: oberras, Bruce

Arthur replied, "It is so. Doesn't your own heart feel the same about me?"

The queen answered, "Of course it does—but there is at this very hour of the night a knight from Rome who is passing through the town of Usk on his way here. Have no doubt that you will find him preeminent in courage and prowess. He is mounted on a steed to which no other can be compared in vigor, value, or grace. His armor is impenetrable, and no one withstands the blow of his right arm. And lest you think I declare this to you lightly, look for the sign: he will send to me a gold ring and three thousand-pieces as well as two horses by mid-morning."

Arthur, aware that she had never deceived him in any prediction whatever, still decided to test this information without her knowledge. For it was his custom that whenever he heard of any strong man presenting himself, he would challenge that man, so that by single combat he could display the greater worth.

So a little later when the queen had drifted off to sleep, he got up, armed himself, mounted his horse, and took as his companion for the encounter only Kay, his seneschal. He came upon the Knight of the Surcoat halting at some little stream flooded by the runoff of the storm; he was looking for the crossing of the ford and cursing the delay. Actually because he was confused by the foul fog of the night, he had decided on the deep channel of the river.

Sighting him by the gleam of his armor, Arthur shouted, "Where did you come from, you who wander over this countryside in the dead of night? Are you a fugitive, a bandit, or a spy?"

5

10

15

20

25

103

Cui Miles cum tunica armature, "Erro quidem ut viarum inscius;
sed nec exulis me fuga agitat, nec predonis rapina instigat, nec
fraus insidiantis occultat." Arturus, "Loquacitate niteris;
nosco versuciam tuam; e tribus que predixi te unum calleo. Ni
igitur quantocius depositis armis te mihi ultro tradideris me   5
tue absque mora nequicie vindicem sencies." Et ille, "Vercordis
et timidi animi est qui ante bellum fugam inierit, aut qui
priusquam necessitas exegerit se adversario submiserit. Si
autem meorum armorum adeo teneris cupidus; eorum obtestor
virtutem, te ipsa duris comparaturum colaphis." Hoc autem modo 10
verbis inter eos ad minas et contumelias prorumpentibus, Arturus
furore exasperatus, quasi rivum jam transiturus et in eum
irruiturus equum calcaribus ad cursum coegit. Cui Miles cum
tunica armature obvius factus, protensa ac demissa lancea in
ipso transsitu eum impulit et mediis undis versis vestigiis   15
dejecit; sonipedemque ad se cursu delatum per lora corripuit.
Successit Kaius dapifer vindica[36r,col.2]turus dominum suum
et admisso equo cum Milite cum tunica armature congreditur,
sed eodem pacto et ipse super Arturum in una congerie primo
ictu prosternitur. Equum autem eius Miles cum tunica arma-   20
ture invexa haste cuspide ad se detraxit. Ipsos vero
incolumes noctis servavit obscuritas. Quique equites illuc
venerant; domum pedites cum non parvo dedecore redierunt.

---

5. quantocius: repeated in MS 8. exegerit: exigerit MS, Bruce
17. vindicaturus: syllable dica doubled MS

To him the knight replied, "I wander because I do not know the roads. No flight of an exile drives me, no pillage of a bandit tempts me, nor does deceit cover any trickery."

Arthur answered, "You rely on your quick tongue. I see your game. I know too well that you have to be one of those three I named. So without more ado, lay down your arms. Unless you give yourself up to me utterly, you will learn immediately that I am the scourge of your wickedness."

The knight responded, "Anybody is foolish and fainthearted who starts to run before the fight, or who gives in to his enemy before he must. If, however, you still want my arms, I swear to their power; I'll match you for them, blow for blow."

So words exchanged between them erupted into threats and abuses, and Arthur, goaded to fury, made ready to cross the river, spurred his horse to the encounter, and rushed blindly at him. The Knight of the Surcoat, waiting for him with drawn and couched lance, drove at him in the ford itself and knocked him into the middle of the river. Backing up, he caught hold of his struggling horse by the reins. Kay the Seneschal, wanting to avenge his lord, spurred his horse and met the Knight of the Surcoat, but just as before, with the first blow he was piled on top of Arthur in a single heap. The knight, using the point of his lance, pulled the horse toward him. The darkness of the night had saved Arthur and Kay from being harmed. Those two who had come to this place as knights returned home as foot-soldiers with no little disgrace.

Arturus vero cubile repetiit. Quem regina Gwendoloena frigore
rigidum, et totum tum imbre, tum rivi undis madefactum quo tam
diu moratus complutusque fuisset interrogat. Arturus, "Afforis
in curia tumultum ac si certancium percepi ad quos egressus; in
eos pacando moram feci, nimboque ingruente me contigit complui." 5
Regina, "Sit ut dicis. Verum quo abieris quidve actum sit; meus
in crastinum nuncius propalabit."

Miles autem cum tunica armature fluviolum minime
transgressus, nec cum quibus habuisset conflictum conscius; ad
quendam vicinum pagum divertit ibique hospitatus est. Summo vero 10
diluculo ad Urbem Legionem tetendit. A qua duobus miliariis
quendam nactus puerum, cui famularetur interrogat. Cui puer,
"Regine," ait, "exsto nuncius cuius archana proferre mandata
mihi incumbit officium." Et ille, "Faciesne," ait, "quod tibi
injunxero?" Puer, "Presto sum quod placuerit." Miles cum 15
tunica armature, "Hos," ait, "duos sume [36v,col.1] sonipedes et
eos mei ex parte deduc regine, utque mee probitatis insigne
gratanter accipiat in pignore rogita amicicie." Anulum eciam
aureum cum iii aureis eidem deferendum proferens suum nomen
edidit, seque e vestigio eum prosecuturum intimavit. Nuncius 20
autem qui sibi injuncta sunt exequitur. Aureos accepit
cornipedesque secum abduxit.

14. mihi MS: mih, Bruce 21. autem: doubled in MS

Arthur, in fact, climbed back into bed. Queen Gwendoloena asked him, stiff as he was with cold, soaked not only by the rain but also by the river water, where he had been for so long and why he was so wet.

Arthur replied, "I thought I heard some sort of commotion outside in the courtyard; I figured it might be some of my men fighting, so I went out. It took a while to settle, and I was drenched in the rain."

The queen answered, "Whatever you say. Truly, wherever you went and what took place my messenger will tell me in the morning."

The Knight of the Surcoat, having crossed the shallowest part of the water and not realizing with whom he had done battle, turned toward the nearby village and found lodging. At the first light of day, he hurried on toward Caerleon. About two miles down the road he noticed a boy and asked who employed him.

The boy told him, "I am a messenger of the queen, whose personal instructions it is my duty to carry out."

And the knight said, "Will you do what I shall require of you?"

The boy replied, "I am at your service."

The knight said, "Take these two horses and lead them for me to the queen as my gift so that she may accept gladly the proof of my prowess in pledge for requesting friendship."

Handing him the gold ring and the three pieces of gold to be carried to her as well, he told him his name and declared he would follow him on the road. The messenger did what had been asked of him. He accepted the gold items and led the horses with him.

Gwendoloena autem regina ut futuri prescia in arcis
prerupto stabat culmine viam prospectans que ad Usce ducebat
oppidum. Que duos equos cum suis adducentem falleris suum
eminus contemplata redire nuncium, rem intellexit, ilico
descendit ac ei jam regiam ingredienti obviavit, puer vero   5
negocium lepide peragit, mandata pandit, transmissa tradit,
Militemque cum tunica armature jam affore predicit. Ad cuius
nomen regina subridens, dona suscipit, gracias agit, et equos
thalamo inductos ante lecticam regis Arturi adhuc quiescentis
utpote qui noctem totam insompnem laborando duxerat statuit.   10
Sompnoque excito, "Domine," ait, "ne me commenti nota argues,
ecce anulus et aurei, quos hodie mihi transmittendos nocte
promisi. Insuper et hos duos dextrarios mihi destinavit quos
eorum sessoribus illo fluviolo obrutis, hac nocte predictus
miles se conquisisse mandavit." Rex autem [36v,col.2] Arturus   15
suos equos recognoscens, pudore consternitur id videns
propalatum quod haberi autumabat secretam.

Egressus est deinde Arturus ad nobilium colloquium; quos
ad conventum pro causis instantibus accitos ea die adesse
jusserat. Cum quibus dum ante aulam sub umbra fraxini   20
resedisset, ecce Miles cum tunica armature equitans valvas
ingreditur. Cominusque in ipsius regis Arturi procedens
aspectum, eum cum consident i regina miliciaque salutat.
Arturus vero non ignarus quis esset, ei trucem vultum
pretendebat, indignanciusque respondebat. Interrogat tamen unde   25

---

3. falleris MS: phaleris, Bruce   6. mandata MS: mandato, Bruce
19. accitos: acscitos MS, Bruce

Meanwhile, Queen Gwendoloena, aware of what was going to happen, stood on the wall of the castle watching the road that led to the town of Usk. When she observed from a distance her messenger returning, leading two horses with all their trappings, she understood the situation and, descending quickly, met him as he entered the hall. The boy transacted the business gracefully, revealed his instructions, delivered the things sent, and announced that the Knight of the Surcoat was about to arrive. The queen, smiling at the name, accepted the gifts and thanked him. She ordered that the horses should be led into the bedroom right to the couch of the king, who was still resting since he had spent the whole night awake and active.

Having roused him from his sleep, she said, "Lord, lest you accuse me of fabricating what I know, see the ring and the gold which yesterday I promised must be sent to me today. Moreover, the knight I foretold last evening has presented to me these two horses which, having overthrown their riders at that river, he cmomandeered for himself."

King Arthur, recognizing his own horses and seeing disclosed what he had hoped to be kept secret, was consumed with shame.

Then Arthur went out to the assembly of nobles he had ordered to come together on that day for pressing concerns. As he sat before the hall under the shade of an ash tree with his people,* the same Knight of the Surcoat entered the gates on horseback. Approaching the presence of King Arthur, he greeted him along with the queen and knights sitting nearby.

Arthur, not unaware of who he was, turned a grim face toward him and responded quite bluntly. He asked about his

5

10

15

20

25

ortus, quo tenderet, quidne illis regionibus quereret. Ille
autem se Romanum esse militem, et quia eum ut Marte pressum
audierat indigere milicia, sibi laturum advenisse presidia,
simulque imperialia detulisse mandata. Thecam igitur signatam
protulit apicesque regi porrexit. Arturus autem litteris   5
acceptis seorsum a turba secessit recitarique jussit. Quarum
testimoniis cum carte monimentis perceptis indiciorum quoque
pallio scilicet et anulo signis prolatis valde obstupefactus
est, quodque omni desiderio verum affectabat existere, hoc ex
ingenti leticia eum videlicet suum esse nepotem nequivit   10
credere. Huiusque rei mansit incredulus, donec eius utroque
convocato parente, Loth rege Norguuegie Annaque regina qui forte
cum aliis ducibus jussi advenerant; rei fidem diligenter
[37r,col.1] ab eis discuteret et indagaret. Quibus id verum
fatentibus eumque suum filium indiciis cognitis adhibito   15
sacramento asserentibus, Arturus incredibili exhilaratur gaudio,
virum tam multimodis imperatoris fultum preconiis, tantarumque
probitatum prelatum titulis sibi ex insperato tanta
propinquitate conjunctum. Ex industria tamen nil ei inde
propalandum censuit, usquequo aliquid preclari penes se   20
patrasset facinoris.

Ad conventum ergo reversus eumque ante omnes convocans,
"Tuo," ait, "amice, in presenti presidio non egeo, in quo
probitas an inercia magis vigeat prossus ingnoro. Magna mihi

---

9. quodque MS, quod, Bruce 15. indagaret: indigaret MS, Bruce
19. conjunctum MS: conjunctum esse, Bruce

origin, where he traveled, what he sought in these regions. The man replied that he was a Roman knight, and that since he had heard Arthur was pressed by war and in need of knights, he had come to offer his services, and that furthermore he had brought imperial mandates. He then handed the sealed coffer and document to the king. When Arthur had received the letter, he withdrew from the assembly and ordered it to be read. On receiving the testimony of the document along with the records of proof and the pallium and signet ring offered in evidence, he was greatly astonished. All this he strove with every desire to regard as truth. Out of immense joy he simply could not believe the fact that this man was indeed his nephew. He remained incredulous of the matter till both parents had been summoned--Loth, King of Norway, and Anna, the Queen--who, it happened, were there, summoned along with the other nobility. He exacted the truth from them and rigorously tested the facts. They confessed that it was all true, that he was indeed their son, and their testimony was witnessed and attested by special oaths. Arthur was exhilarated with incredible joy that the man upheld in so many ways by the emperor's commendations and by a great reputation for exalted prowess was, as a final surprise, related to him by close kinship. Nevertheless, he purposely ordered that none of this should be revealed to the knight till he had accomplished some outstanding exploit in his presence.

So returning to the assembly and calling the knight before everyone, Arthur said, "Your help, friend, I do not need at the present time; I do not know precisely whether prowess or awkwardness flourishes more in you. I have a band of knights

sat militum exstat copia, incomparabilis probitatis robore et virtute predita, inertemque et timidum probis et bellicosis ingerere eorum est animos a solita audacia et probitate velle enervare. Tui similium eciam absque stipendiis mihi permaximus sponte militat numerus inter quos mea excellencia nisi prius 5 merveris te nec eciam censendum existimat." Ad hec Miles cum tunica armature eius dictis exasperatus respondit, "Gravem repulsam et inopinatam injuriam tibi famulari cupientem me a te contigit incurrere qui quondam quandoque nec multis exoratus precibus nec magnis conductus opibus, te dicioribus dignabar 10 obsequendo assistere. Nec me non reperturum dubito cui serviam; dum eciam si tantum animum intendero, quibus imparem leviter [37r,col.2] inveniam. Verum quia me huc adduxit affectus experiunde milicie et si hinc discessero, timiditati ascribetur et inercie tali condicione me tue milicie dignum censeas numero, 15 si illud in quo tuus totus defecerit exercitus, solus peregero." Arturus, "Meum," ait, "contestor imperium, si compleveris quod pacisceris, te non solum eis ascribam verum omnium amori preponam." Regi itaque ac ipsius universis optimatibus sentencia placuit; eumque prelibata condicione penes se 20 retinuit.

Non dies bis seni transierant, et causa huiusmodi in expedicionem Arturum proficisci compulit. In aquilonari parte Britannie erat quoddam castellum puellarum nunccupatum, cui tam decore, quam generositate preclara et famosa jure dominii 25 presidebat puella, amicicie nexibus Arturo admodum copulata.

8. te MS: te non ascribendum, Bruce   13. quibus: omitted Bruce.
18. pacisceris: pacisseris MS, Bruce

of such incomparable prowess, endowed with such strength and and courage, that to include a clumsy and cowardly one among the skillful and daring is to risk weakening their spirit from its customary boldness and aggressiveness. An enormous number of knights like you serve me voluntarily without stipend, among whom, unless you should first show you deserve it, my decision stands that you should not even be enrolled."

To this the Knight of the Surcoat, goaded by his words, replied, "By offering to serve you, I have incurred from you a grave rejection and an unexpected injury--I, who heretofore was deemed worthy to offer to come to your aid inasmuch as I was not dissuaded by numerous entreaties nor influenced by great wealth. I do not doubt that I will find someone whom I may serve; yet even if I try, I will not easily find your equal. Indeed, since a desire for military challenge brought me here, and if I should depart from here it could be ascribed to cowardice and clumsiness, on the following condition you might consider me worthy to be one of your band of knights: that I alone accomplish something in which your whole army shall have failed."

Arthur answered, "My reply is this decree: If you should accomplish what you have bargained, I shall not only enroll you among them but indeed set you to be loved above them all."

The plan pleased the king and all his nobility as well, and he kept the knight at his court for the present under the agreed condition.

Not twice six days had passed when an occasion of this sort compelled Arthur to set forth an expedition. In the northern part of Britannia was a certain castle called "Castle of the Maidens," which a young woman, who was noted as preeminent for her grace and nobility, governed by right of lordship.

Huius prestanti forma et pulcritudinis magnitudine, quidam rex
paganus captus et ab ea despectus, ipsam in predicto oppido
obsidebat, jamque compositis machinis, comportatis et erectis
aggeribus, quasi eam expugnaturus et obtenturus imminebat.
Cuius dum juges incursus, et cotidianos assultus illa preferre   5
nequivisset, misso nuncio sibi suppecias Arturum advocat, sese
turri inclusam exteriori vallo occupato, haud mora hostibus
dedendam asserens, nisi cicius presidia conferat. Arturus autem
eius discrimini oppido [37v,col.1] metuens, virtutem milicie
confestim congregat, instruit, et ordinat; perfeccioneque   10
parata, licet maxima constrictus formidine, quo accitus fuerat
iter arripuit. Multociens enim cum eodem rege commiserat et
congressus fuerat sed semper repulsum et devictum eum constabat.
Illi vero obsidionem petenti, alius prepeti cursu occurrit
nuncius, qui cum cesarie super genas dilaniatus, municipium   15
quidem expugnatum illam autem captam intimat et abductam;
mandantemque sibi ut quo amore eam dilexisset in prosperis, tunc
ostenderet in adversis. Manubiis igitur honustos, Arturus
adversarios insequitur extrema eorum agmina que inprovisa
autumabat furibundus aggreditur sed malo ab illis omine exceptus   20
est. De eius quippe adventu predocti, armati et ordinate
incesserant, validiores ad munimen tocius exercitus posteriori
in turma locaverant, qui subito impetu non facile perturbari
poterant.

---

9. discrimini: Bruce suggests a lacuna here. metuens: first syllable
doubled. 10. congregat: cogregat MS, Bruce 11. accitus: acscitus MS,
Bruce 15. super: added Bruce.

114

She was allied to Arthur by the deepest obligations of friendship. A certain pagan king, captivated by her graceful bearing and great beauty and having in turn been rejected by her, had besieged her in her own fortified town. Already, since the siege machinery had been constructed and transported to the site and the mounds to support it built up, he was threatening to storm the castle and seize her. Since she knew she could not bear up under the unremitting attacks and daily assaults, she sent a messenger and begged Arthur to come to her aid. As she was barricaded in her tower and the farther wall had already been breached, she deemed it necessary to surrender very soon to the enemy unless he brought up reinforcements immediately.

So Arthur, fearing the peril of the young woman in her castle, at once mustered, armed, and drew up the ranks of his knights; and fully prepared, though consumed by great dread, he began the march to the place where he had been summoned. Many times, it is true, he had encountered and fought this very king, but it had always resulted that he was repulsed and beaten.* As he was approaching the siege, a second messenger arrived, running with hair loose about his cheeks, who reported that the pagan king had razed the city and had seized and carried off the lady. The messenger continued to plead for his mistress that the love King Arthur had held for her in prosperity he would now show her in adversity. Arthur pursued the enemy burdened with plunder. He fell furiously upon their rear guard where he thought them least protected, but because of an unfortunate omen, he was intercepted by them. Having been thus warned of his approach, they repulsed him armed and in battle order. To protect the line they had placed the more experienced warriors in the rear guard, which would not then be easily thrown into confusion by sudden attack.

115

Ad tumultum igitur extremi agminis priores revertuntur
phalanges, Arturumque ex omni circumdantes latere; comprimunt
impellunt et affligunt. Hic pugna acerrima commissa, stragesque
cruenta utrimque illata est. Ac Arturus medio hostium
conspectus gremio valde conterebatur anxiebatur, et   5
fatiscebatur, nique viam gladiis aperiens fugam cicius
maturasset, cum omni [37v,col.2] cesus pessumdaretur exercitu.
Fuge itaque salutem commisit, sanius ducens salvus fugiendo
evadere quam ultro se ingerendo periculum incurrere.

Belli autem exordio, Miles cum tunica armature remoto et   10
prerupto loco secesserat, quis prelii exitus commilitones
maneret contemplaturus. Quos ubi fuga lapsos comperit, Arturo
cum prioribus fugienti obviavit, atque ei subridendo insultans,
"Numquid," ait, "O rex, cervos an lepores agitis, qui sic
passim dispersi per avia tenditis?" Cui Arturus indignatus   15
respondit, "Hic tuam satis probitatem expertam habeo; qui
aliis pugnam adeuntibus, te nemoris abdidisti latebris." Nec
plura locutus adversariis instantibus pertranssiit. Miles
autem cum tunica armature in eius singulos militum sibi
obviancium lepide et ridiculose cavillatus, insequentibus hosti-   20
bus occurrens eorum se catervis seviens ingessit. Quorum con-
fertos et constipatos cuneos ad instar hyberne procelle per
medium penetrans neminem quidem lesit, nisi quem sibi fortuna
resistentem obtulit. Ut autem regalem aciem intuitus est calcaribus illico subductis cornipedem admisit, et lancea vibrata,   25
splendidum ferrum sub cavo pectore inopinus regi intorsit.

---

5 anxiebatur: anriebatur MS, corrected in margin. 20. ridiculose:
rediculose MS, Bruce

His front ranks, instead, were brought to confusion by the unexpected strength of the enemy's rear guard; and they, surrounding Arthur's men on all sides, contained them, pressed them, and shattered them. Here the bitterest battle was fought and bloody slaughter was inflicted on both sides. And Arthur, having been in the very lap of the enemy, was being pressed back most strongly, demoralized and exhausted; and unless by cutting his way out he could immediately retreat, he would be slain and his entire army cut down. He therefore gambled on the deliverance of flight, calculating it wiser to run to safety than to succumb to the disaster hanging over him.

At the beginning of the engagement, the Knight of the Surcoat had withdrawn to a high, remote lookout in order to see what might befall the fellowship of knights during the course of battle. When the retreat revealed the disaster to him, he confronted Arthur fleeing with the first wave, and laughing at him, shouted bitingly, "Tell me, O King, do you pursue deer or perhaps rabbits that you go scattered this way along the paths?"

To him Arthur replied indignantly, "I have sufficient proof of your great prowess that you, while others are involved in battle, have removed yourself to some secret hiding places of the forest." Without further words he rode off, the enemy in pursuit.

The Knight of the Surcoat, taunting with jeers and slurs every single one of the knights he encountered, turned to attack the pursuing enemy. He rushed raging upon the advance patrols, penetrating through the tight and strong formations into their very midst like a winter storm—he injured no one except those who offered him resistance.

When he saw the royal guard, he instantly spurred his horse forward; with lance couched, the unexpected assailant ran the gleaming point into the hollow of the king's chest.

Quo moribundo corruente puellam per lora corripit, ac via qua
venerat cicius regredi cepit.

Agmina autem que regem circumsteterant suum dominum sui
medio [38r,col.1] peremptum confusa, discedentem cum clamore
presecuntur strictisque gladiis impetunt et invadunt. Ipse in   5
omnes et omnes in eum irruunt. Eminus alii in eum tela
jaculantur, ceteri ancipiti mucronum acie eum sine intermissione
contundunt, ut sicut pluvie inundacio, sic ictuum in eum
conflueret multitudo. Ille autem hos super illos obtruncatos
deserens, suum semper iter agebat. Sed multum impediebatur,   10
quod non tantummodo se, sed eciam illam oportebat defendere.
Non longe autem perampla et profunda distabat fovea duarum
provinciarum terminos dirimens. Ideoque limes et divisio
illarum dicebatur finium; cuius angustus aditus et transitus non
nisi unius admittebat ingressum. Ad hanc igitur Miles cum   15
tunica armature accelerans et deveniens, puellam intra fosse
municionem tuto inmisit, precipiens se donec rediret in remota
ibidem operiri. Iterum adversariorum se usque insequencium
inmergens cuneis repellebat, fugabat, dispergebat, ac more
leonis catulis amissis infremens in eos crudeli strage seviebat. 20
Nullus eius impetum pertulit, nec aliquis quem gravis moles eius
dextre attigisset, indempnis abivit. Quocumque se convertebat
ac si a facie tempestatis ab eo dilabebantur, quos jugiter ad
exicium agens sine pietate trucidabat. Nec destitit donec omnes
in fugam conversos, omnes [38r,col.2] perniciei traderet, dum   25
pars eorum se ex preruptis rupibus precipites darent, pars
obstantibus fluctibus se sponte involverent; et ipse superstites
cede dilaniaret.

---

9. obruncatos: obtrunctatos MS, Bruce 21. quem: quam MS, Bruce

118

Having thrown the dying man to the ground, he seized the young
woman by her horse's bridle and at once set out to return the
way he had come.

But the guard which surrounded the king, thrown into
disorder on seeing their lord struck down in their midst, with a   5
shout cut the invader off; and swords drawn, they charged and
set upon him. They rush at him together, and he at all of them.
From a distance some throw spears at him; from all sides others
strike at him ceaselessly with their blades. Like a rain storm
the multitude of blows beat upon him. Still, he continued on   10
his way, leaving them cut down. But he was greatly hampered
because he had to defend not only himself but his lady. Not far
distant was a broad and deep fosse marking the boundary between
two provinces.* By this was the limit and division of their
boundaries decreed. It had only a narrow access and its bridge   15
allowed only one person to cross at a time. To this place,
then, the Knight of the Surcoat raced, and arriving there, he
sent the lady to safety within the fortifications of the fosse,
ordering her to remain hidden from sight until he returned.
Once more plunging into the ranks of the pursuing enemy, he   20
turned them back, put them to flight, and dispersed them.
Roaring like a lion bereft of its cubs, he raged cruel slaughter
upon them without mercy. Not one of them bore up under the
attack nor did any who came in contact with the massive power of
his right arm go away uninjured. Wherever he turned, they were   25
scattered as from the blast of a tempest.

The powerful one continually slashed them to death without
pity. Not withdrawing until all of them had been routed, he
marked all for death: some flung themselves from the steep
banks, some by choice threw themselves into the obstructing   30
waters, and the remainder he himself cut to pieces in a
massacre.

119

Miles igitur cum tunica armature absque sui detrimento habita victoria capud regis diademate insignitum abscidit, ipsius vexillo infixit, ac in sullime erigens; ad regem Arturum cum sua puella prope remeavit. Ovansque aulam ingressus, qua rex Arturus super belli infortunio tristis et merens residebat,   5
"Quonam sunt," exclamat, "O Rex, tui famosi athlete, de quibus te adeo jactabas neminem eorum parem virtuti? Ecce capud viri, viri quem cum omni suorum copia militum solus vici et prostravi, a quo tot tuorum pugillum milia, tociens proh pudet fugari et enervari. Tuumne adhuc me militem dignaris?" Recognoscens autem   10
Arturus regis capud sibi pre omnibus odiosi sibique dilectam ab inimicorum manibus ereptam letatus, eius in amplexus irruit, atque, "Revera dignandus et optandus es miles," respondit, "precipuisque donandus honoribus. Verum quia adhuc pene incertum habemus quis nobis adveneris, enucleacius rogo insinua,   15
que tibi natalis tellus, a quibus originem trahas, et quo censearis nomine." Et ille, "Rei quidem habet veritas, me Gallicanis in partibus Romano senatore progenitum, Rome [38v,col.1] educatum, Miles cum tunica armature sortitum vocabulum." Arturus, "Plane falleris, fideque caret tua   20
estimacio; et te hac opinione prossus deceptum noveris." Miles, "Quid ergo?" Arturus, "Ostendam," inquid, "tibi tue propaginis seriem, cuius rei cognicio tui laboris erit remuneracio."

7-8. viri, viri MS: Bruce omits one.

The Knight of the Surcoat, having gained victory without injury to himself, cut off the head of the pagan king with the royal diadem still in place, fastened it on his standard and, raising it on high, returned to King Arthur with the lady by his side.   Exulting, he entered the hall where King Arthur,   5
depressed and grieving at the misfortune of war, was seated.

He cried out, "Just where, O King, are your famous champions of whom so long you boasted that no one is their equal in courage? See the head of the man I alone conquered and laid low, along with the entire force of his knights.   He was the   10
king who with a handful put to flight and terrified so many thousands of your men so often that it is shameful! Do you consider me worthy to be your knight?"

Arthur, joyous, recognizing the head of the king hateful to him beyond all others and the young woman so dear to him   15
rescued from the hands of the enemy, ran to embrace him and replied, "You are truly worthy to be chosen as a knight, and you must be granted special honors! Nevertheless, since till now we have been uncertain who you are who have come to us, I ask you to explain more in detail where your native land is, from whom   21
you trace your lineage, by what family name you are listed?"

And the other replied, "The truth of what I have told you holds.   I was born in the region of Gaul, fathered by a Roman senator. I was educated in Rome, and 'Knight of the Surcoat' is what I happen to be called."   25

Arthur returned, "You are plainly mistaken and what you have thought true cannot be confirmed; you must learn that, in a word, you have been deceived in this information."

The knight asked, "How so?"

Utroque igitur ipsius parente presente, Loth scilicet rege
et Anna regina Norwegie, sibi ab imperatore directas litteras
jubet afferri, allatasque in aure multitudinis vulgi et nobilium
recitari. Quibus intelligentibus universis perlectis cum
ingenti stupore incredibilis omnium mentibus innascitur leticia,   5
talique sobole beatos clamitabant parentes. Tunc rex Arturus
eum hylari vultu intuens, "Meum te," ait, "karissime nepotem,
huius mee sororis filium cognoscito, quem talem edidisse non
infamie, sed maximo ascribendum est fortune beneficio."
Subjunxitque, "In puerili quidem etate, 'Puer sine nomine,' a   10
tirocinio autem usque ad presens, 'Miles' es vocatus 'cum tunica
armature'; jam a modo 'Waluuanius' proprio censeberis notamine."
Hec Arturo dicente, terque, quarterque ab omni cetu, "Waluuanius
nepos regis Arturi!" ingeminatum et inculcatem est. A patre
igitur filio ab avo nepote agnito magnitudo gaudii dupplicatur,   15
cum pro amissi recuperatore pignoris, tum pro ipsius
incomparabili virtute et fortitudine. Cetera que virtutum
Waluuanii secuntur [38v, col.2] insignia qui scire desiderat a
sciente prece vel precio exigat. Sciens quod sicut
discriminosius est bellum inire quam bellum referre, sic   20
operosius sit composito eloquencie stilo historiam exarare quam
vulgari propalare sermone.

FINIS

---

21. operosius: operiosius MS, Bruce.

Arthur explained, "I shall show you your lineage. Knowledge of this fact shall be the reward for your deeds."

Thereupon, with both of his parents present, to wit, Loth, King of Norway, and Anna, the Queen, he ordered the letter written by the emperor brought to him and, when it was brought, to be read in the hearing of the multitude of people and of 5 nobles. When all the people were informed and all the documents read, amazement and incredible joy arose with the comprehension of it all, and they proclaimed the parents blessed for such an offspring.

Then King Arthur, gazing at him with joy, spoke: "I 10 acknowledge you, dearest one, my nephew. You are the son of my sister to whom ought to be ascribed the good fortune to have borne such a child not for any disgrace but for the greatest honor." He added, "Indeed at an early age you were called 'Boy with no Name,' and from the time you entered knighthood till the 15 present, 'Knight of the Surcoat.' From now on you will be known as 'Gawain,' your real name."

When Arthur announced this, three times, four times from the entire assemblage "Gawain, nephew of King Arthur" was repeated and echoed. 20

The son, having been acknowledged by his father, the nephew by his uncle, the magnitude of joy is doubled, not only for the recovery of a lost loved one but also for this man's incomparable courage and strength. What other outstanding exploits fall to the share of Gawain, he who desires to know 25 must demand by request or payment from one who knows. Realizing that just as it is more decisive to take part in a battle than to record a battle, even so it is more difficult to compose a history in eloquent style than it is to present it orally in the words of common speech. 30

THE END

123

5. A pallium in the Roman period was a rectangular piece of cloth worn as a cloak. In the medieval period it had become a ceremonial band of white wool worn by the pope and conferred by him on archbishops as a symbol of office. A pallium may also be an altar cloth or a pall. This elaborate piece of cloth is part of the tradition of Gawain's endangered infancy: Les Enfances Gauvain has "le paile ke mot ert beaus" (line 140), the Perlesvaus, "moult riche paine" (Bruce, 1913, p. xxxix).

A voyage to Narbonne from Britannia involves passage of the Straits of Gibraltar. Making this voyage in eight days would mean not only having favorable winds but also navigating the Straits without making port, even at night. Although the text does not elaborate on the difficulties of the voyage, the ports of the Straits of Gibraltar were in Moslem control from the early twelfth century to the last quarter of the thirteenth. The harbor at Narbonne, in use since the days of Roman engineering, was silted up after a storm diverted the Aude River in the latter part of the thirteenth century.

13. Scipio Africanus, also known as Scipio the Elder, was a renowned Roman general who lived from 236 to 183 B.C. Wieber notes that according to Livy (Ab Urbe Condita 44.16.10) the residence of Scipio Africanus was on a site adjoining the Palatine Hill, but that Scipio's house ceased to exist before the Palatium, the Imperial Palace, was built (p. 98).

The emperor endows Viamundus with income property belonging to the Empire as a way of giving him a salary as a government official.

17. The Circus is traditionally a place where public games were held, particularly chariot races, and it may be puzzling to read that this is the site for the tournament for the new knights. Yet "cursus" carries the meaning not only of racing but also of a military charge. The English word "course" reflects the same ambiguity in "race course" and "courser," a war-horse or charger. The noun "course" has the archaic meaning of the charge of opposing knights, or passage at arms.

19. The Equirria were Roman festivals honoring Mars on February 27 and March 14 when horse races were held.

The "ordo equester" or Equestrian Order was a distinguished rank of the Roman Empire bestowed by the emperor, usually for life. It was given by right of birth to sons of Senators, qualified young men of sufficient wealth, and in a few cases, gifted freedmen. The rank of Centurion in the "ordo equester" was particularly distinguished.

21. This is a concise description of a medieval battle formation, showing use of foot soldiers as well as knights. For further reading on military tactics as background for De ortu Waluuanii, see J. F. Verbruggen, The Art of Warfare in Western Europe during the Middle Ages, particularly his summary of the use of knights and foot soldiers by the armies of the kingdom of Jerusalem against the Moslems, pp. 195-97.

27. The plight of the emperor's niece in DOW may have been influenced by the details of the most famous abduction in the fifth century, when the half-sister of Emperor Honorius was abducted by the

Goths at the Sack of Rome. Galla Placidia, whether reluctantly or willingly, married Ataulfus, who had succeeded his brother Alaric as King of the Goths. Later Ataulfus was assassinated. Constantius, commander-in-chief of the Romans, ransomed Placidia and married her. He was raised in rank to Augustus. Constantius was originally from Illyricum.

39. The crimson chlamys is a young man's garment from ancient Greece consisting of a short, oblong mantle fastened on the right shoulder.

61. Kemp (p. 49) includes illustrations of a windvane with a dog carved on it found in Heggen as well as a thirteenth-century carving from Bergen showing the prows of a Norse fleet, some of which are ornamented with similar windvanes.

101. The town of Usk near the ford six miles upstream from Caerleon is still there. The ancient castle on the hill above the town is in ruins but the ruins have been incorporated into homes. The town is primarily a fishing resort because of the salmon in the river Usk. Although the storms and dry periods of the centuries may have changed the bed of the river, there is still a significant shallow area close to the town which would have been an easy place to ford the river; it is a community park where children can safely wade.

109. Arthur has gathered his nobles and his knights outside at Caerleon on the morning that Gawain is expected to present himself. Perhaps the court may be pictured as assembled in the Roman amphitheater, recently excavated and known locally as "Arthur's Round Table," or it may be simply that Arthur felt the need of the ash tree, said in

folklore to protect against spells and enchantments, according to Tom Peete Cross, _Motif-Index_ of _Early Irish Literature_, Item D13852.2.

115. Arthur's difficulty with the raiders from Scotland is also told by Caradoc of Llangarfan, _Vita Gildae_, paragraph 5 (Hugh Williams, ed. and trans., _Gildas_, London: Cymroddion Society, 1901, pt. 2, 400-03). Caradoc records that Arthur eventually killed Hueil, their leader. Gawain is not mentioned.

119. The boundary ditch as described in _DOW_ shares many details with the Roman ruin of the Antonine Wall. If the Castle of Maidens in the north of Britain is identified with Edinburgh Castle, the ditch that marks the boundary that raiding pagan warriors must cross would be the Antonine Wall, assuming that the pagan king ruled a people who lived beyond the realm of Arthur. The part of the defenses of the Wall that survived is the great ditch, impressive even today--awesome in the Middle Ages. Crossing would have been possible by temporary bridges. Gawain rescues the Lady of the Castle of Maidens, races to this defendable point, has the Lady hide in the walls beyond--that is, south--of the ditch, and he proves his prowess by standing off the pagans, one on one.

INDEX OF NAMES

Gawain, named "Waluuanius" by his mother. He is known as "Knight of the Surcoat" until reunion with his family in King Arthur's court. 5

Gormundus, Persian champion at the single combat at Jerusalem. He is too tall for a horse to carry. 83

Guendoloena, Arthur's queen. She is beautiful but also initiated into sorcery. 101

Jerusalem, 21

Kay, the Seneschal, knight who accompanies Arthur to the ford. 103

Knight of the Surcoat, the soubriquet given Gawain because of his crimson surcoat. 19

Lady of the Castle of Maidens, beautiful woman who is chatelaine of the Castle of Maidens and allied to King Arthur. When she spurns the Pagan King, he besieges her castle. 113

Loth, father of Gawain. He is nephew of Sichelm, King of Norway, and a hostage in King Uther's court. 3

Merchants, wealthy men who have come to Britannia from the Mediterranean area seeking trade. They agree with Anna to accept the infant Gawain when he is born and bring him up in their own country. 5

Milocrates, King of the Pirates. He controls the Barbarous Isle and holds the niece of the Emperor of Rome as his consort. 27

Nabaor, the knight on the Barbarous Isle who is the ally and confidant of Milocrates' Queen. 39

Narbonne, city on the Mediterranean coast of France. 5

Odabel, kinsman of the Centurion. He accompanies Gawain on the mission to spy on Milocrates, the pirate king. 33

The Pagan King, would-be suitor of the Lady of Castle of Maidens. When she refuses him, he attempts to abduct her. 115

Persia, 21

The Queen, Milocrates' captive consort on the Barbarous Isle. She is niece of the Emperor of Rome. 27

Rome, 9

Severn River, river flowing into the Bristol Channel. In Roman times
the river was known as the Sabrina, the name of both the river
itself and the Bristol Channel as well. 101

Sichelm, King of Norway. "Sichelm" is the usual spelling in Geoffrey
of Monmouth, Historia Regum Britannia 9.9. The MS of DOW has
"Chelmus," as do some versions of the Historia. 3

Sulpicius, Pope of Rome. He is present at Viamundus' death-bed
confession. "Sulpicius" is not a historical pope, but the name is
also given as the name of the pope in Geoffrey of Monmouth,
Historia Regum Britanniae, 9.11. 13

Usk, town in southeast Wales, six miles from Caerleon. 101

Usk River, river in southeast Wales that flows into the Bristol Channel.
101

Uther, King of Britannia, father of Arthur and Anna. He is portrayed
as the king who consolidates all of the kingdom of Britannia and
gains sovereignty over its bordering kingdoms as well. 3

Viamundus, poor nobleman reduced to beachcombing. He kidnaps the
infant Gawain and begins a new life in Rome with the fortune
provided by Anna for Gawain's support. 7

Waluuanius, a Latin form of "Gawain." 4.